Gold Stars™

PHONICS WORKBOOK

Parragon®

Helping Your Child

- Remember that the activities in this book should be enjoyed by your child. Try to find a quiet place to work.
- Always give your child lots of encouragement and praise.
- Your child does not need to complete each page in one go. Stop before your child grows tired, and come back to the same page another time.
- It is important to work through the pages in the right order because the activities do get progressively more difficult.
- The answers to the activities are on pages 124 – 128.

This edition published by Cottage Door Press, LLC, in 2020.
First published 2017 by Parragon Books, Ltd.

5005 Newport Drive, Rolling Meadows, Illinois 60008

Written by Nina Filipek
Cover art by Irina Avvakumova, used under license from Shutterstock.com
Illustrated by Simon Abbott
Educational Consultant: Janet Rose

ISBN: 978-1-68052-996-8

Printed in China

Selected Contents

Explore Sounds

A snake goes hissssss

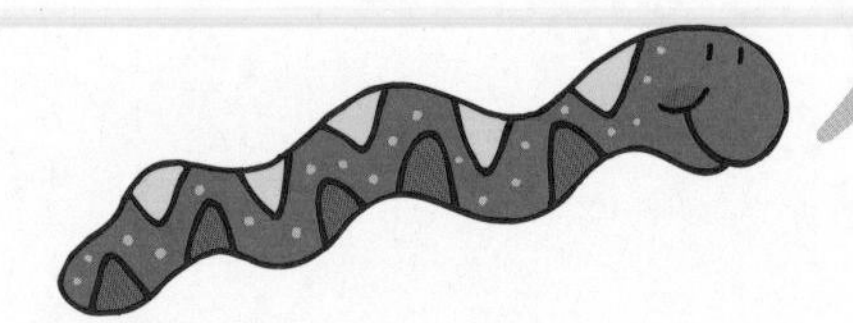

A bee goes buzzzzz

What sounds do these animals make?
Make your own sound effects for each picture below.

Note for parent: Sounds are all around us. Humans and animals communicate through sound.

Make Sounds

What sounds can these children hear in Noisy Town?
Make sound effects for each picture below.

Note for parent: Your child can have fun making up sounds to match these pictures.

Sounds of Music

Make sounds for the music in the band.

The triangles in the band go... **ting, ting, ting!**

The drums in the band go... **bong, bong, bong!**

The cymbals in the band go... **crash, crash, crash!**

The singers in the band go... **la, la, la!**

... All day long!

Note for parent: You could sing the words to the tune of "The Wheels on the Bus Go Round and Round."

Letter Sounds

Each letter of the alphabet has a sound.
Trace over each letter. Start at the red dot and follow the arrows. Say each sound out loud as you write it.

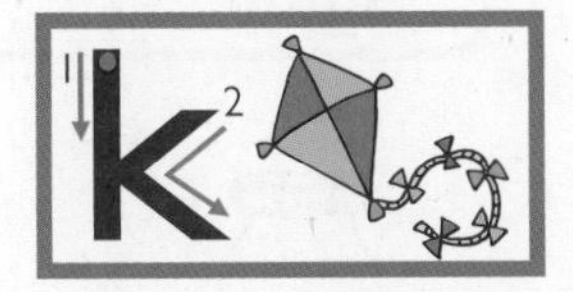

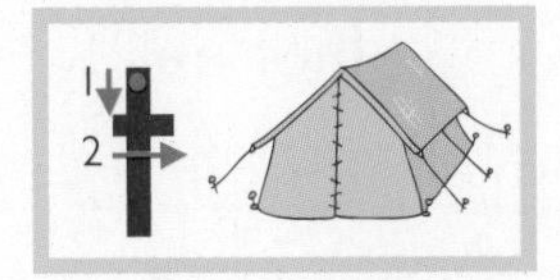

Note for parent: Teachers refer to sounds as phonemes. When we put phonemes together we make words.

Sounding out Letters

Look at the pictures. Say the words. Sound out the beginning letters.

Note for parent: This activity helps your child to practice phonemes. Encourage your child to focus on the phonetic sound of a letter instead of its name.

mug
m
mmm (not em)
nut
n
nnn (not en)
octopus
o
ah (not oh)
pen
p
puh (not pee)
queen
q
kwuh (not kew)
ring
r
rrr (not aar)
sun
s
sss (not ess)
10
ten
t
tuh (not tee)
umbrella
u
uh (not you)
van
v
vvv (not vee)
web
w
wuh (not double-you)
box
x
ks (not ex)
yo-yo
y
yuh (not why)
zebra
z
zzz (not zee)

Say the Sounds: s, a, t, p, i

Say the sound of each letter.

Look at the big picture and name something beginning with each of these sounds:

s a t p i

Note for parent: These are the easiest letters to start with and they are among the most common.

Blend to Make Words

Blend the letter sounds to find out what Rob Robot is saying. Say the words.

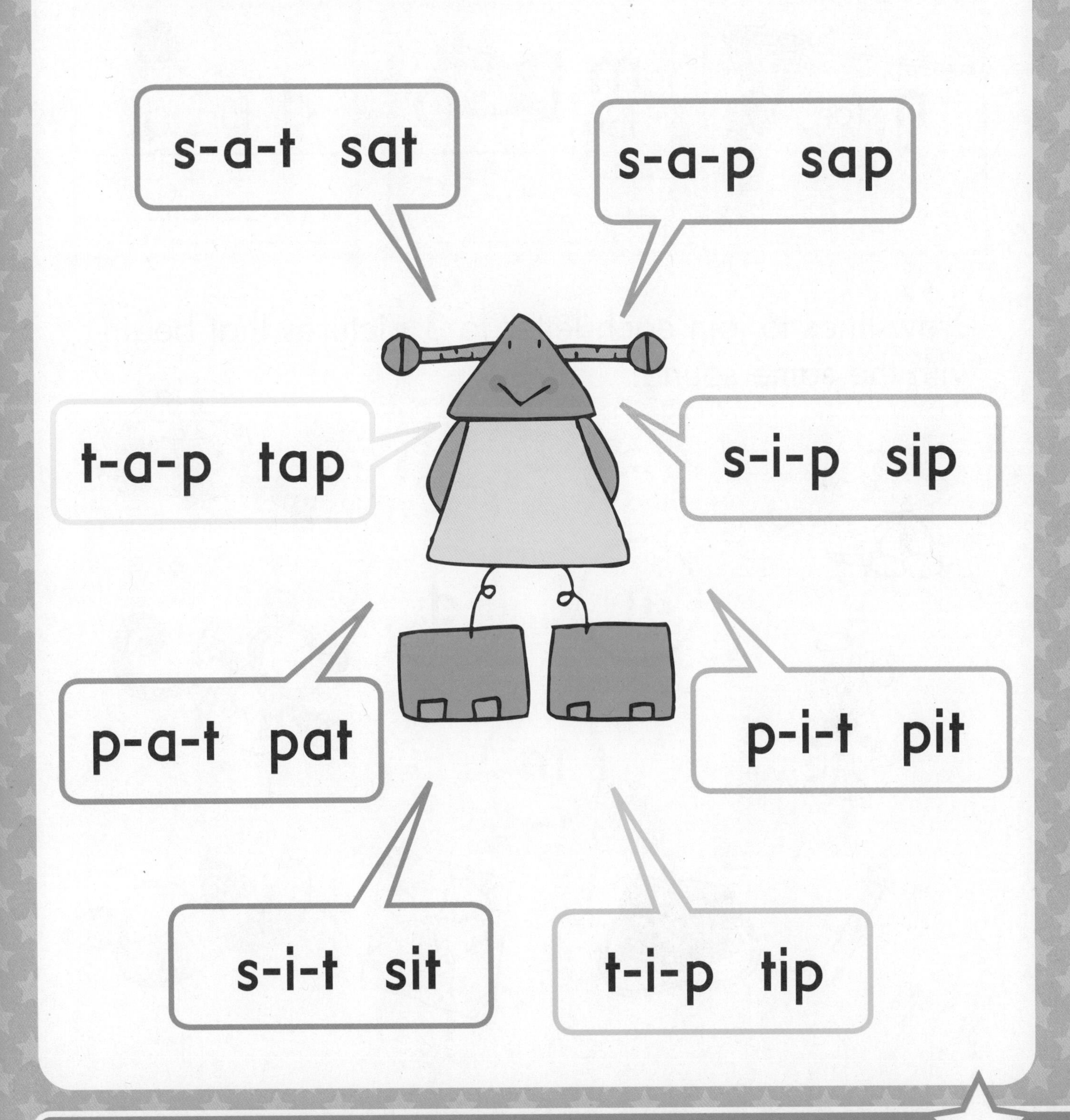

Note for parent: To blend means to join the separate sounds together until the word sounds right.

Say the Sounds: n, m, d

Trace over the letters. Say the sound of each letter as you write it.

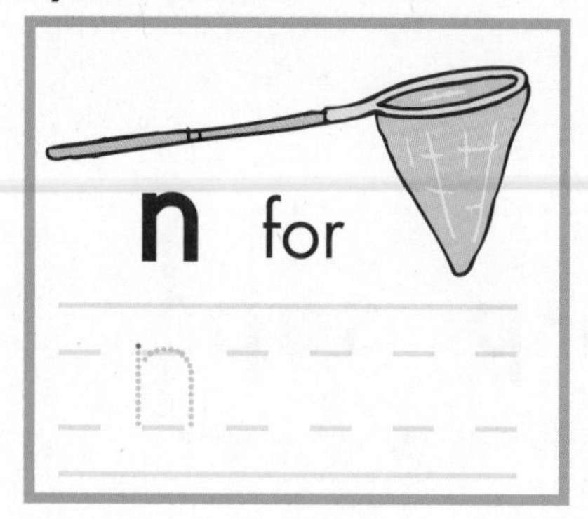

Draw lines to join each letter to 3 pictures that begin with the same sound.

Note for parent: Help your child to find the correct match, e.g., if they say "birds" instead of "nest" then ask, "Can you think of another word beginning with n?"

Blend to Make Words

Blend the letter sounds to read the words on each mat.
Find 2 words that are **exactly** the same.
Draw a circle around them.

Now find words that end in the same sound.
Draw lines to join them.

Note for parent: Read aloud the rhyming words with emphasis on the final sounds.
Encourage your child to listen for the rhyme.

Word Builder

Letter sounds are put together to build words.
Read the words in each word wall below.

a
a n
a n d

a
a n
a n t

a
a n
p a n

a
a m
S a m

a
a t
p a t

Note for parent: Look for smaller words within longer words, e.g., am in Sam.
Can you find any little words in your child's name?

Word Search

Find 5 words in each word search below. Look across and diagonally. Draw a circle around each word you find in the word search box.

man
sat
tap
tan
map

t	a	p
s	a	t
m	a	n

t	i	p
s	i	t
p	i	n

pin
sit
pip
tin
tip

Note for parent: Word games are a fun way of practicing literacy skills.

Say the Sounds: g, o, c, k

Trace over the letters. Say the sound of each letter as you write it.

Circle 2 pictures in each box that begin with the same sound.

Note for parent: The letters c and k sound the same in these words. Point out the different sound of o in orange and owl.

Blend to Make Words

Blend the letter sounds to read the words.

Which of these words has a capital letter? Why?

Note for parent: Tell your child that names begin with capital (or upper-case) letters. Practice writing the capital letter that starts your child's name.

Say the Sounds: e, u, r

Trace over the letters. Say the sound of each letter as you write it.

Circle the sound you can hear in the **middle** of each word below.

pen **e** or **u**

red **e** or **u**

sun **e** or **u**

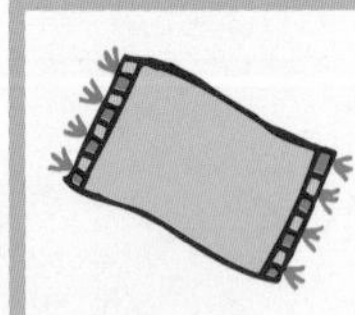

rug **e** or **u**

ten **e** or **u**

cup **e** or **u**

net **e** or **u**

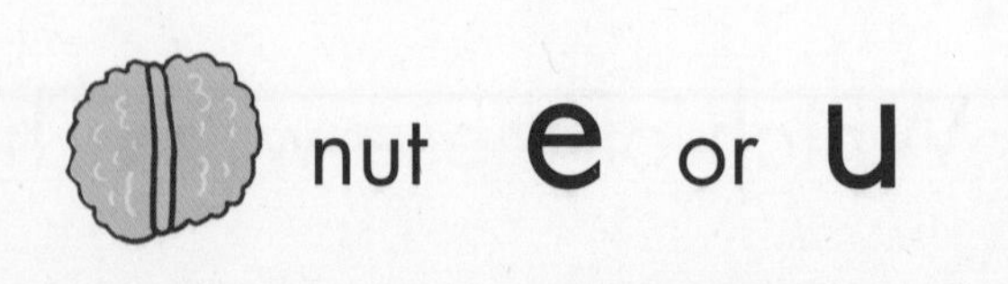

nut **e** or **u**

Note for parent: At school, your child will learn how to read words made up of three letters: a consonant, a vowel, and a consonant. These are CVC words.

Say the Sound: ck

Sometimes we put **c** and **k** together. Blend the letter sounds to find out what Ron Robot is saying. Say the words.

Draw lines to join the words that rhyme.

Note for parent: ck is pronounced as one sound. It can also be found in the middle of words, e.g., pocket.

Say the Sounds: l, h, b, f

Trace over the letters. Say the sound of each letter as you write it.

Sound out the letters in these words. Read the words.

Note for parent: Sound out the letters in each word. Then blend to say the word.

Match Letters to Pictures

Say the sound of the letter in the middle of each circle. Draw lines to match each letter to 3 pictures in the big circle that begin with this letter.

Note for parent: Prompt your child to find the answer. Praise their efforts. What is obvious to an adult may not be obvious to a 5-year-old.

Word Builder

Blend the sounds together to make words. Draw lines to join the sounds to the complete words. The first one has been done for you.

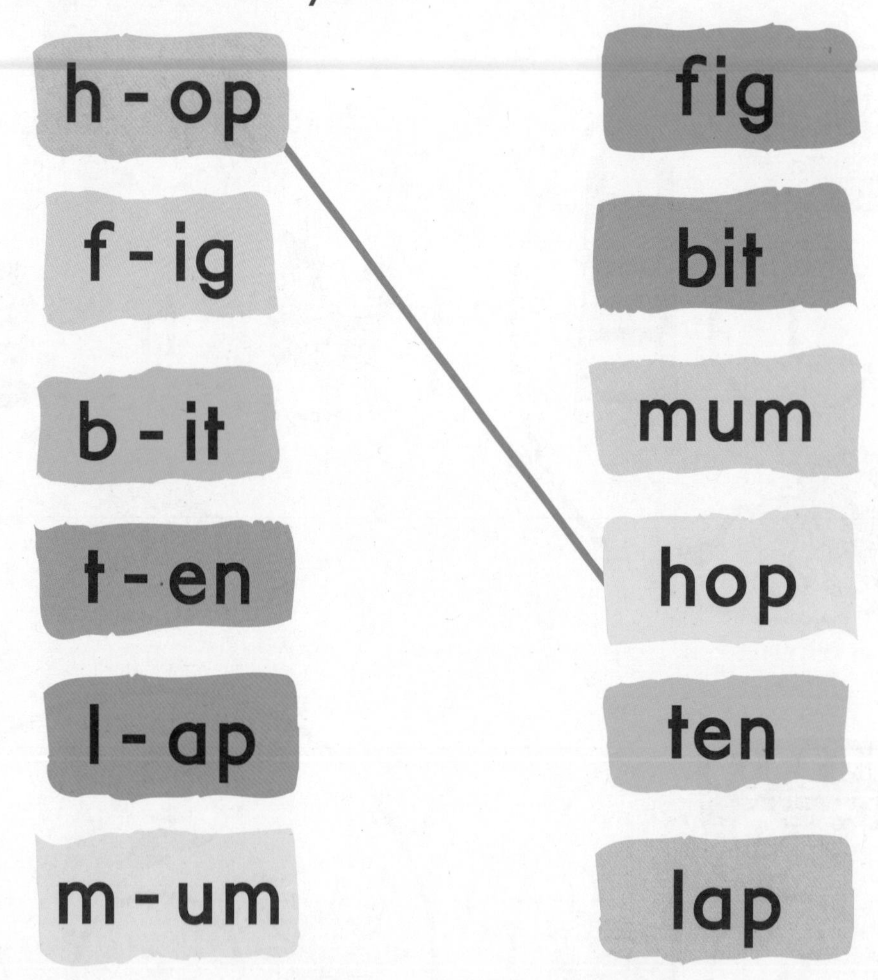

Make some silly words by joining these sounds. Say the words.

b - im   t - as   l - ib

s - uz   f - ep   h - of

Note for parent: The silly words are a good test of your child's phonic skills.

Complete the Words

Blend the sounds together. Trace the letters to complete the words.

b - at bat

h - ad had

b - eg beg

h - en hen

b - ig big

h - id hid

b - op bop

h - ot hot

b - un bun

h - um hum

Note for parent: The short vowel sounds of a, e, i, o, and u appear in the words above.

Sound story: ss, ll, ff

Trace over the letters to complete the words.
Say the sounds as you write them.

ss ll ff

Ask an adult to read the story to you.

Miss Hill rings the bell.
The class plays pass the ball.
Bill falls in the grass.
He hears a hiss!
Then a huff and puff!
"Don't fuss," says Miss Hill.

"But, Miss!" says Bill.
"It's behind you!"
"Run, class!" shouts
Miss Hill.

Note for parent: As you read aloud, point to the words with your finger. Then go back to the text and encourage your child to read the double-letter words.

Tricky Words

Blend the letter sounds to read the story.
Say these tricky words:

I go no to the of on

The bus can **go to the** top
of the hill.

I can **go to the** top.

I can hop **on the** top.

The dog can run **on the** top.

Oh **no, the** bus hit a rock **on the**
top **of the** hill.

Oh **no, the** bus cannot **go**!

Note for parent: The tricky words appear in bold. Repetition of these words in the story will help your child to remember them.

Compound Words

Join two words to make one word.
Trace over the letters.

sun - set	sunset
sun - tan	suntan
hand - bag	handbag
hill - top	hilltop
up - on	upon
bob - cat	bobcat
pad - lock	padlock
ruck - sack	rucksack

Note for parent: These words are known as compound words. There are further examples later in the book.

Hickory, Dickory, Dock

Trace over the letters.

ck ck ck ck ck

Write **ck** in the spaces in the words and say the nursery rhyme.

Hi_ _ory, di_ _ory, do_ _,

The mouse ran up the clo_ _,

The clo_ _ stru_ _ one,

The mouse was gone,

Hi_ _ory, di_ _ory, do_ _!

Note for parent: Teach your child some well-known nursery rhymes. The language patterns found within them are a good literacy tool.

Read It Yourself

Read the words underneath each picture.

a pig in the mud

a dog in the sun

a cat in a hat

a rat on the run!

Draw your own picture in the last box to match the last description.

Note for parent: Encourage your child to write captions for their drawings.

Find the Word

Look at the pictures and find the correct word to complete each label. Draw lines to join the words.

pans

mugs

eggs

dogs

balls

Note for parent: Discuss these common pairings.

Read the List

Read the items on the list. Tick each one as you find it in Sid's suitcase. Is anything missing?

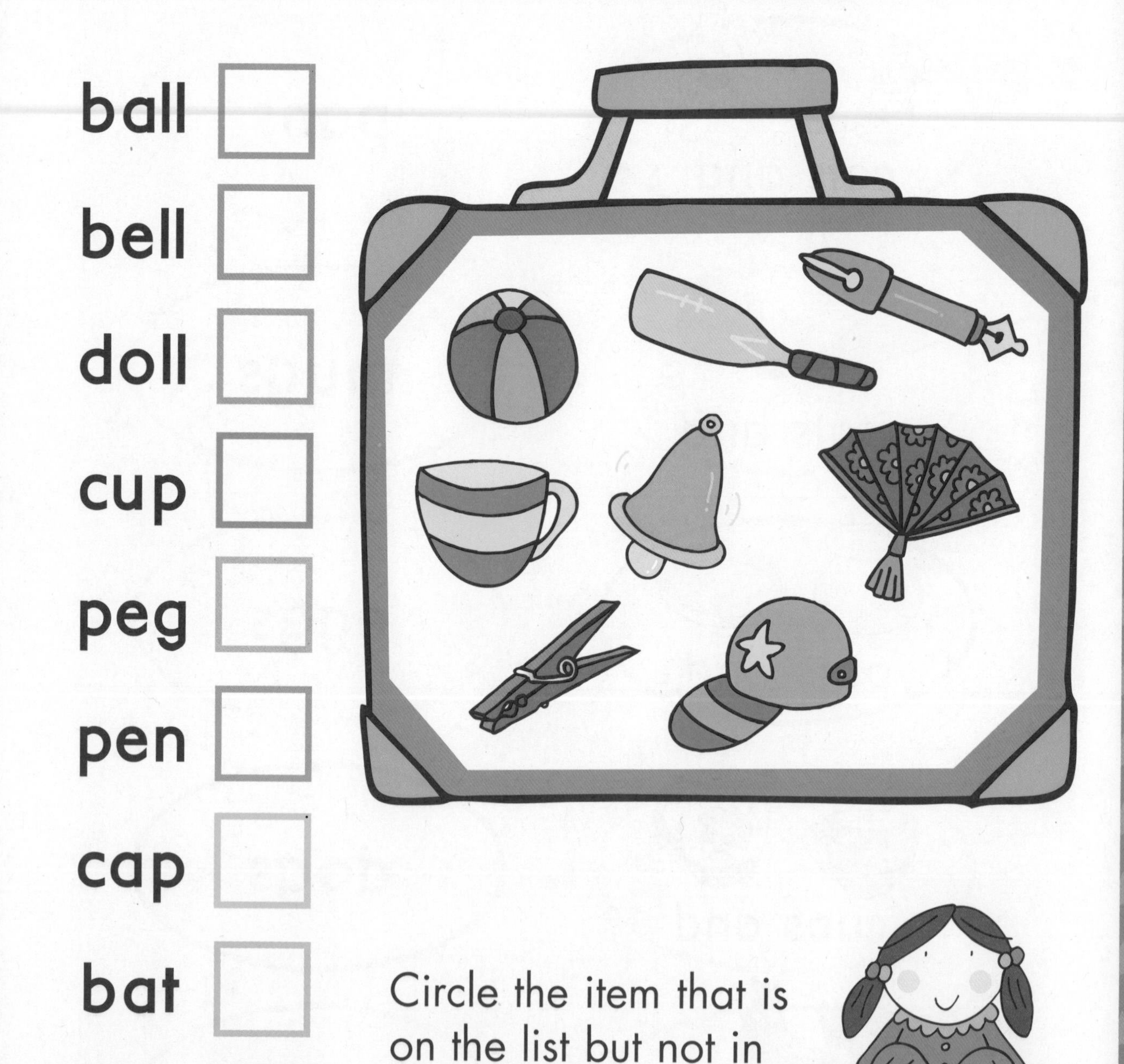

- ball ☐
- bell ☐
- doll ☐
- cup ☐
- peg ☐
- pen ☐
- cap ☐
- bat ☐
- fan ☐

Circle the item that is on the list but not in his suitcase.

Note for parent: This activity will revise phonemes already introduced.

Circle the Word

Circle the correct word to match each picture.

ten or den

dog or cog

deed or seed

fan or can

mop or top

sock or lock

Color the Real Words

Say each letter sound, then blend the sounds together to read the word. Which words are silly and which are real? Color the real words in red.

Note for parent: This activity provides further practice in blending sounds and decoding unfamiliar words.

Name the Robots

Say each letter sound, then blend the sounds together to read the words.

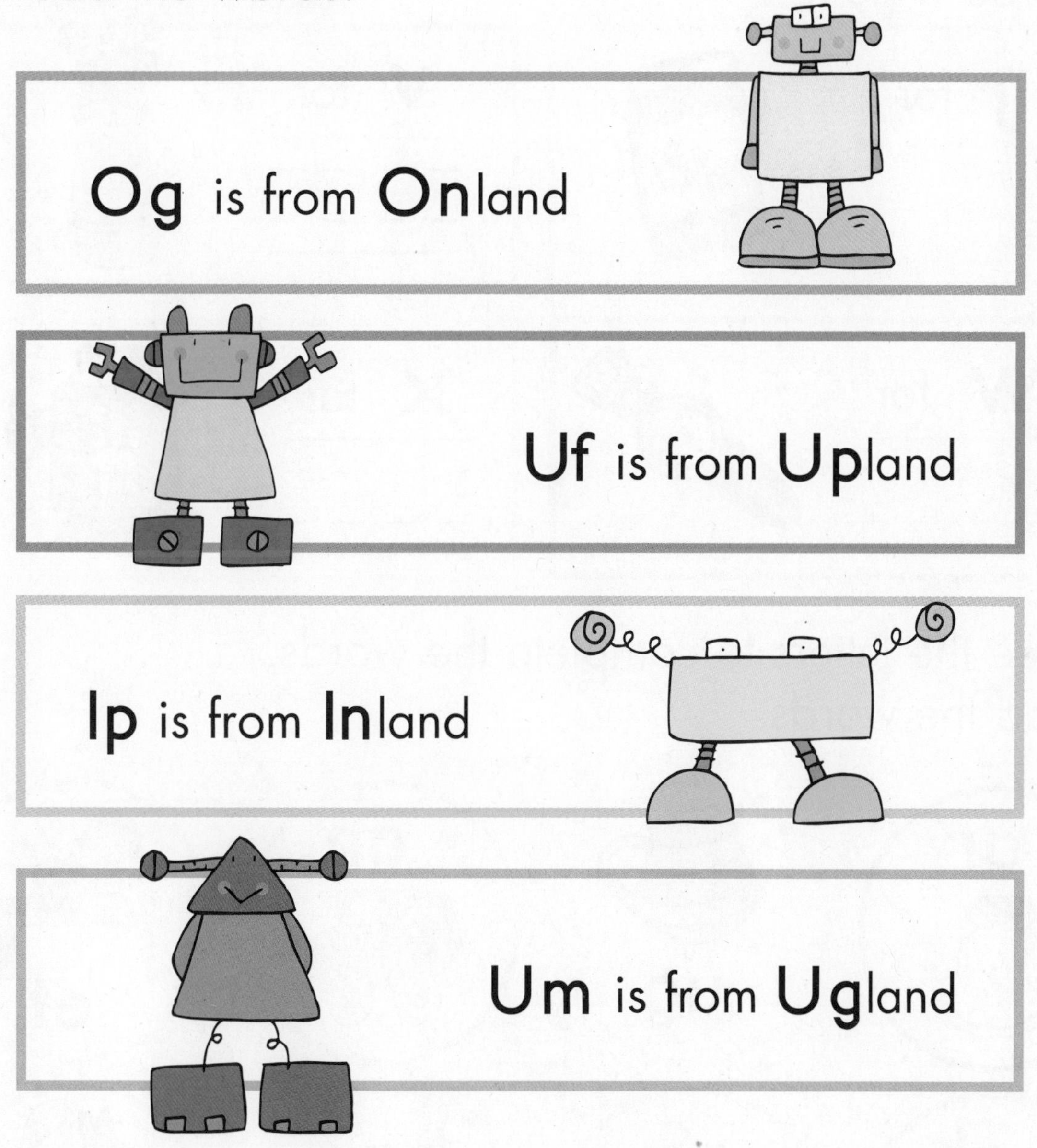

Who is from Inland?

Who is from Onland?

Note for parent: Help your child to spot the difference between the beginning sounds Og and On, etc.

Say the sounds: j, v, w, x

Trace over the letters. Say the sound of each letter as you write it.

Trace the letters to complete the words.
Read the words.

Note for parent: Few words in the English language begin with x. It is more common as a final sound.

Pet Names

Match the pets to their owners. Their names start with the same letters. Draw lines to join them.

Jack and... Bix 

Raj and... Van 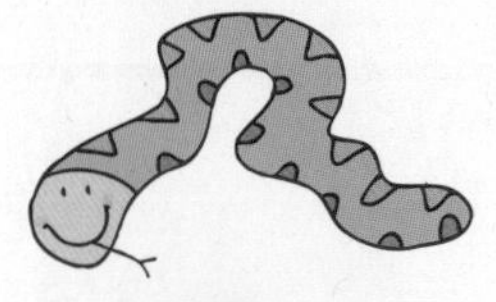

Tim and... Jaws 

Pip and... Mug 

Vin and... Pop 

Bex and... Rav

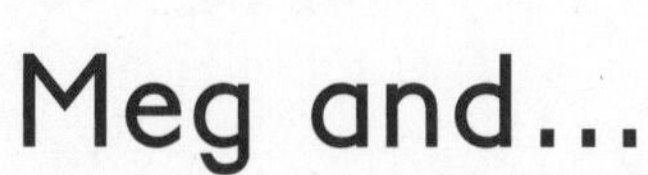
Meg and... Tom 

Note for parent: Alliteration (a string of words with the same beginning sound, e.g., Jack and Jaws) is a common literary device.

Say the sounds: y, z, zz

Trace over the letters. Say the sound of each letter as you write it.

Note for parent: Ask your child which are the last two letters of the alphabet. The answer is y and z, of course!

Say the sound: qu

Trace over the letters. These two letters make one sound when they are together.

qu qu qu qu qu

Write **qu** in the spaces in the words and say the rhyme.

Qu is for _ _ iver and _ _ ake,
But not for shiver and shake,
Qu is for _ _ arrel and _ _ ibble
But not for dribble and drabble
Qu is for _ _ ick and _ _ ack,
Queen and _ _ iet,
Quarry and _ _ ite,
Quiz and _ _ est,
Are there any more qu's?
Join the _ _ eue!

Note for parent: The letters q and u are usually found together in the English language.

The Alphabet

Draw lines to join the letters in alphabetical order from a to z. Say the alphabet – say the names of the letters, not the sounds.

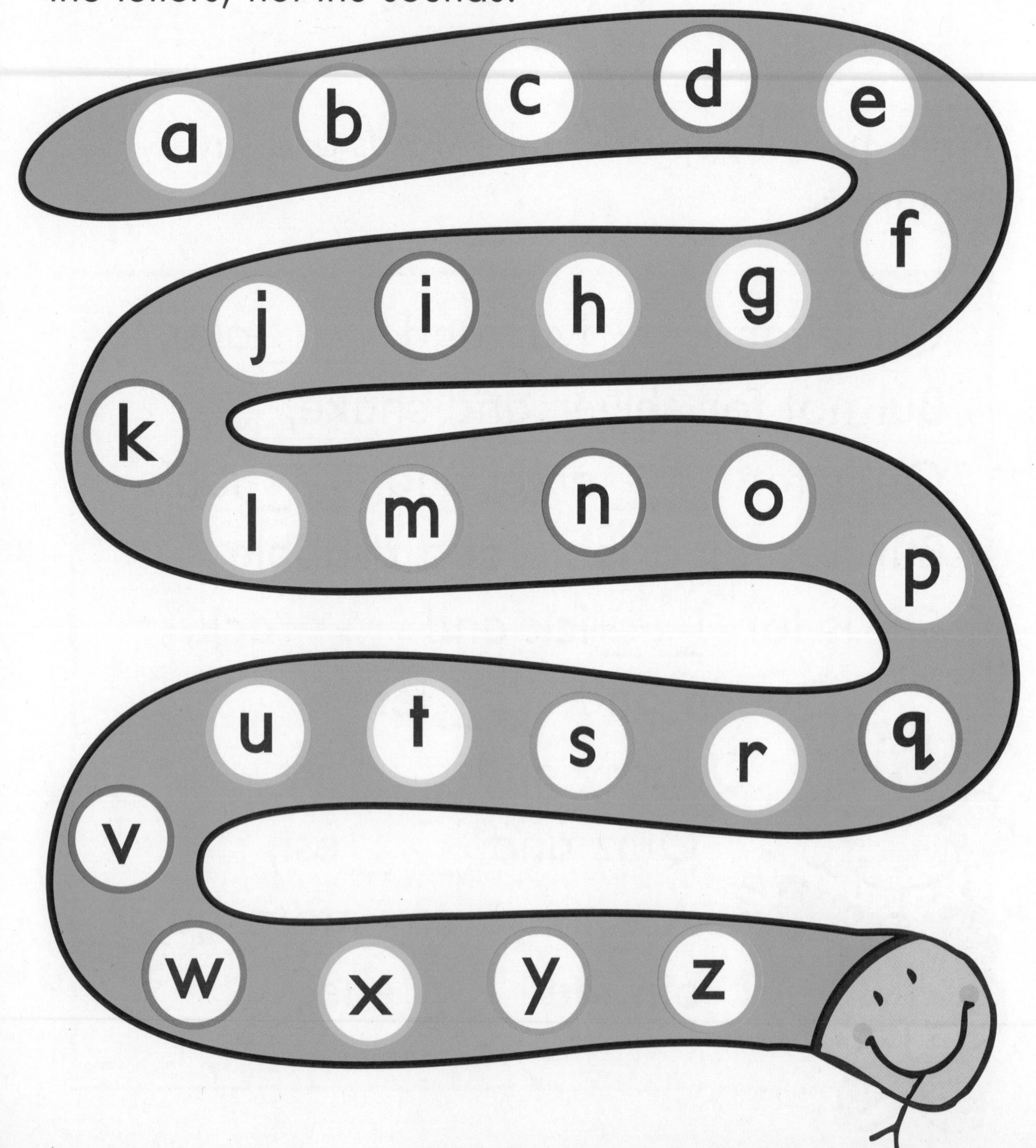

Note for parent: Letter sounds are different from letter names. The sounds are how we pronounce a letter in a word. The name is what we call the letter.

Capital Letters

Here are the capital letters. They are used for people's names and the names of countries, towns, rivers, days and months, and much more.

Trace over the capital letters. Start at the red dot and follow the arrows.

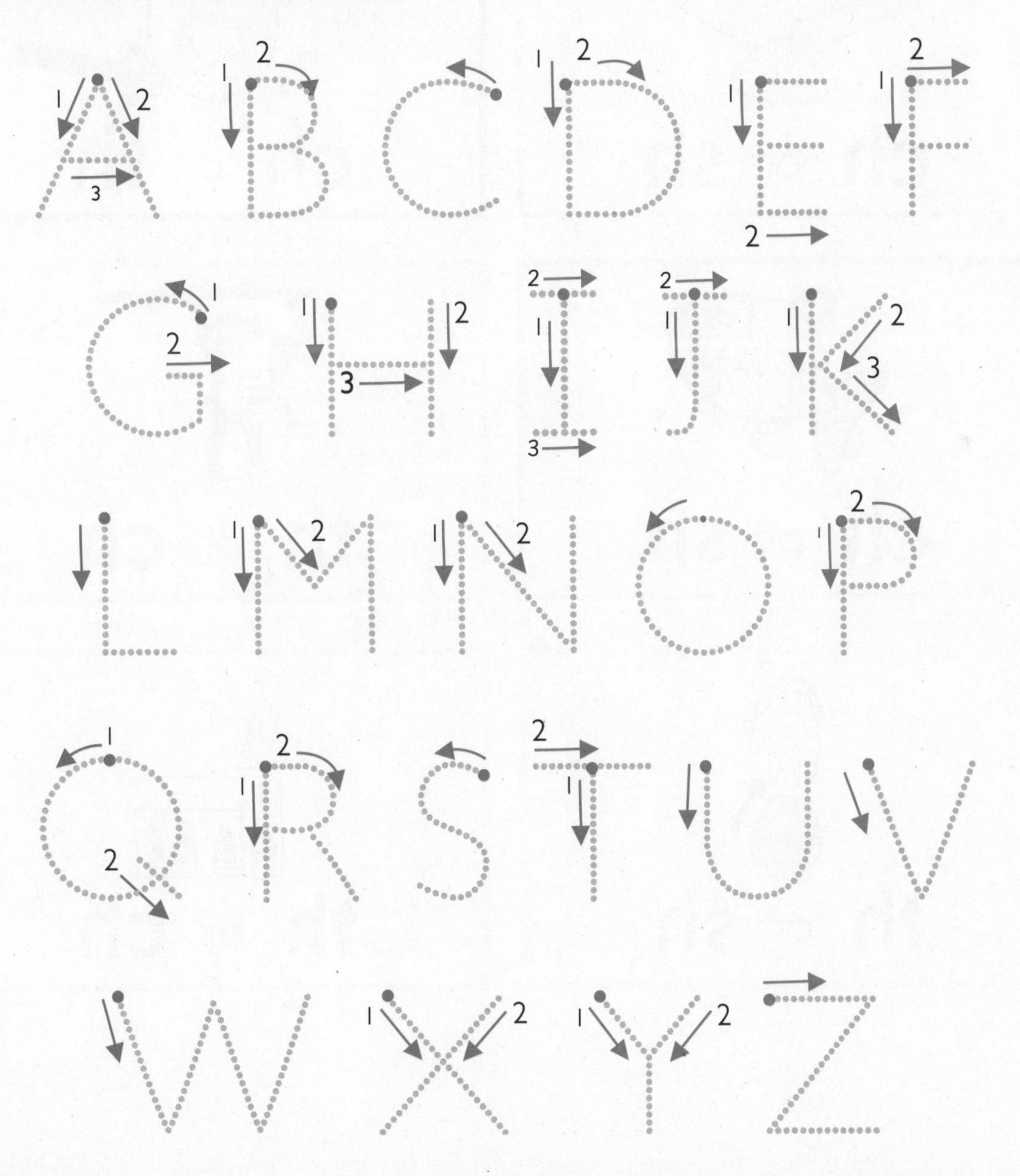

Note for parent: Practice writing your child's name in both lower-case (with a capital to start) and upper-case letters.

Say the sounds: ch, sh, th

Say the name of each picture. Circle the sound you can hear in each word.

ch or **sh**

ch or **th**

ch or **sh**

th or **ch**

th or **sh**

th or **ch**

Note for parent: This activity introduces common consonant digraphs. A digraph is two letters that together make one sound.

Trace the Letters

Trace over the letters.

ch sh th

Trace the letters to complete the words.
Read the words.

dish

thick

think

shop

chill

ship

chip

rush

thin

wish

shed

chick

Tricky Words

Say these tricky words. They are not easy to sound out so you have to learn them by sight. They are important because we use them a lot!

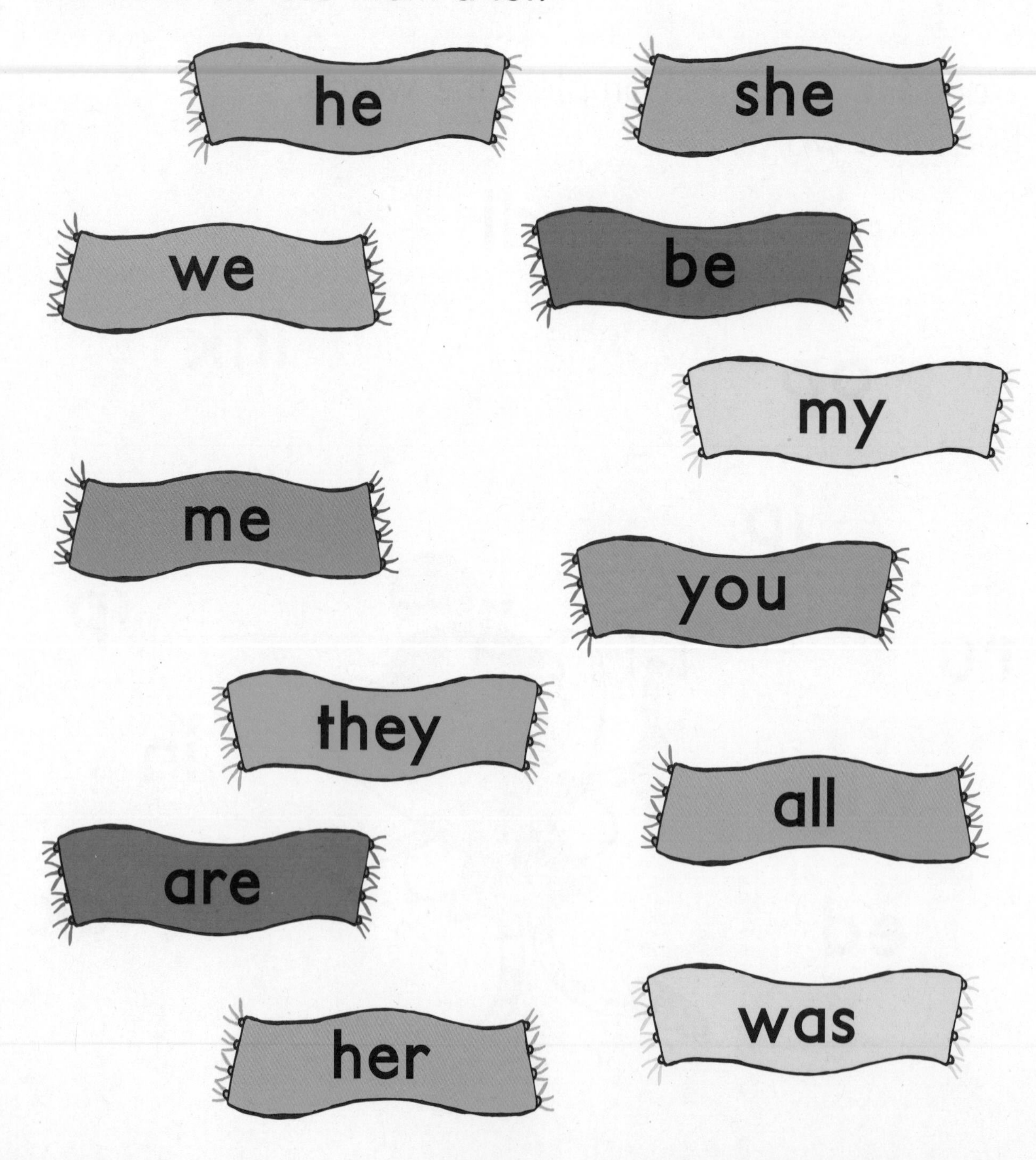

Note for parent: There is no easy way of learning these words. But with practice and familiarity your child will begin to recognize them on sight.

Read the Speech Balloons

Read the speech balloons to find out what they are saying.

Note for parent: What do you think the children are talking about? Encourage your child to think of possible scenarios.

Letter Blends: Beginnings

Blend the sounds to read the words below.
The first two letters make one sound.

For example: **fr-o-g**

Try these:

Note for parent: The first two letters in these words are consonant digraphs. Together they make one sound.

Letter Blends: Endings

Blend the sounds to read the words below. The last two letters make one sound.

For example: **j-u-mp**

Try these:

l-a-mp

y-e-lp

s-i-nk

c-a-rd

d-i-sk

b-u-mp

s-o-ft

d-e-sk

Note for parent: The last two letters in these words are consonant digraphs. Together they make one sound.

Three Billy Goats Gruff

Read this story with an adult. Try to read some of the words yourself. When you come to a picture, predict what the word might be.

Once upon a time 3  s
had to cross a 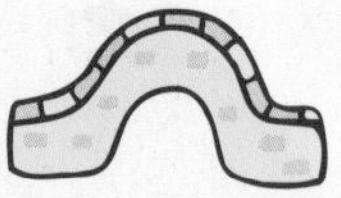 .
Clip-clop, clip-clop, went the  s.
A troll jumped onto the 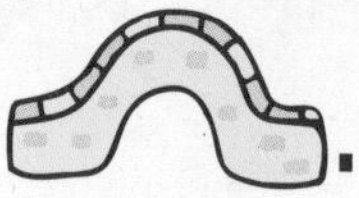 .
"I am a troll, fol-de-rol!
Get off my 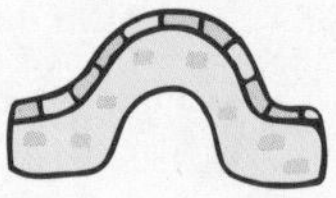
or I will eat you all!" said the troll.
The biggest  said, "No, you will not!"
and butted the troll off the 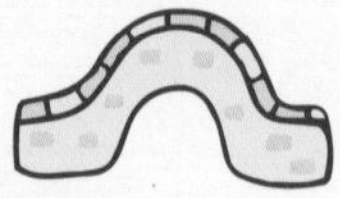 !
The 3  s crossed the 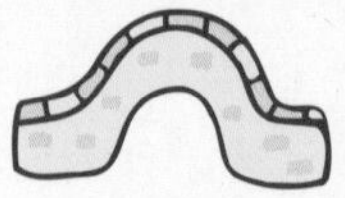 safely
and lived happily ever after.

Note for parent: Encourage your child to try to read some of the words they have already learned in this book.

Rhyme Time

Blend the sounds in the words and try to read the poem yourself.

Note for parent: Help your child to sound out the letters to read the words.

Word Builder

Make some silly words by joining these sounds.
Say the words.

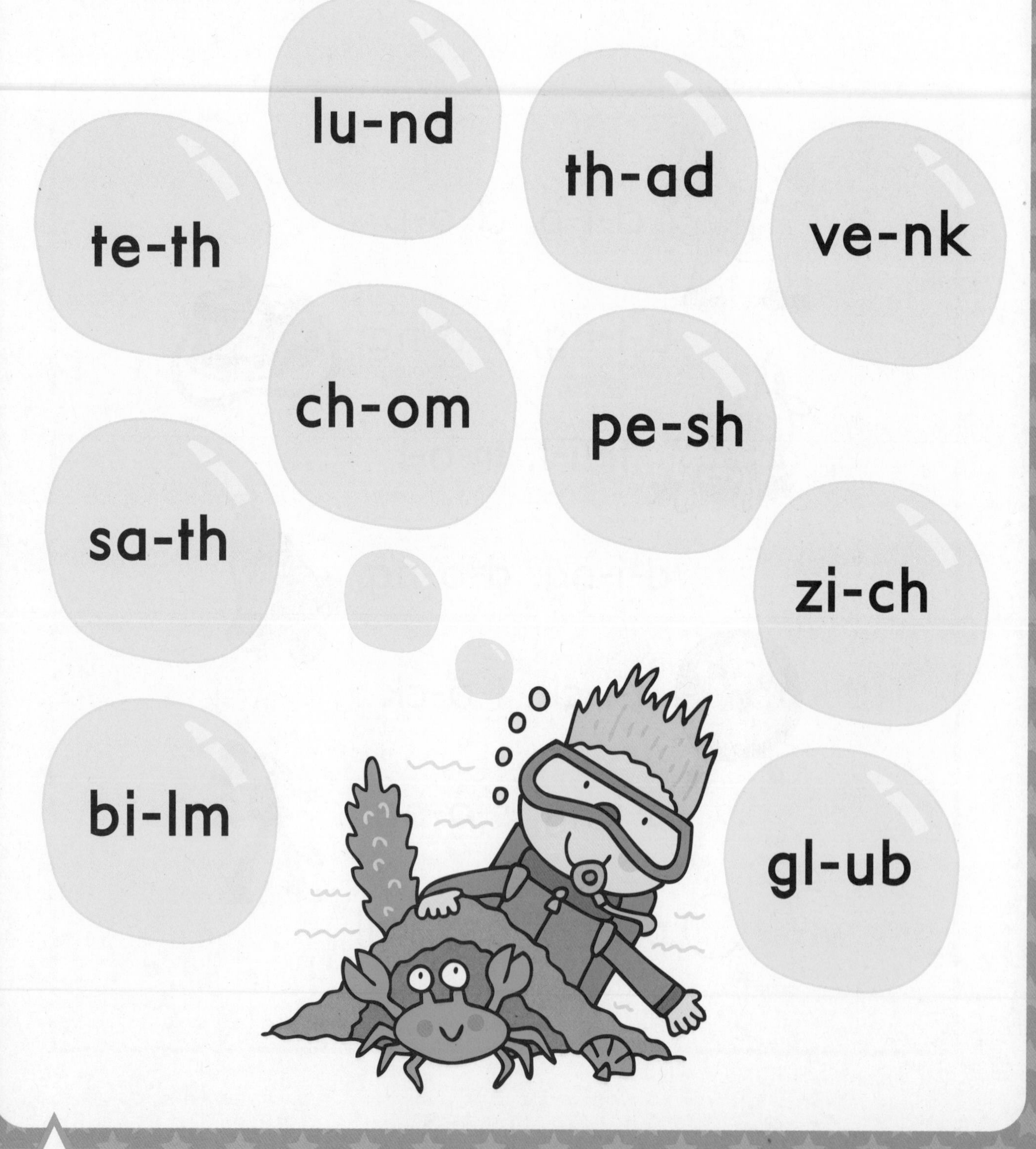

Note for parent: Reading these silly words is a useful test of your child's phonics skills.

Vowels and Consonants

The alphabet has 5 vowels. They are: **a**, **e**, **i**, **o**, **u**. Find the vowels and color them in red. The other letters are called consonants. Color these in a different color.

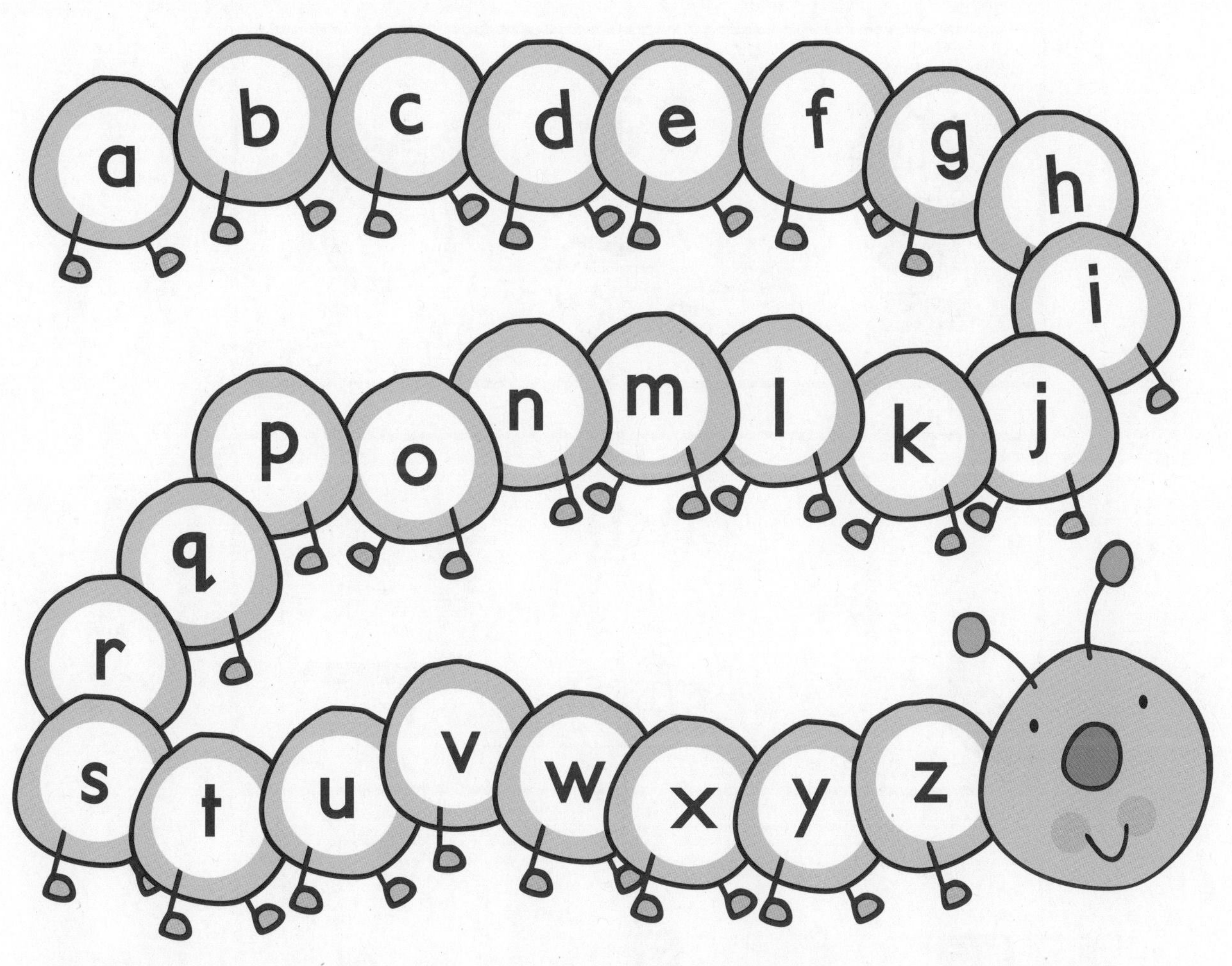

Write your name in the space below—with each letter in a circle. Color the vowels in your name in red and the consonants in another color.

Note for parent: Your child needs to know what the vowels and consonants are. Most words in the English language contain vowels and consonants.

Say the Sounds: ng, nd, st

Say the sound of the letters in the middle of each box. Draw lines to connect the sound to two pictures in the box that contain this sound.

Note for parent: Occasionally you may need to prompt your child to come up with the right connections.

Trace the Letters: ng, nd, st

Trace over the letters.

ng nd st

Trace the letters to complete the words.
Read the words.

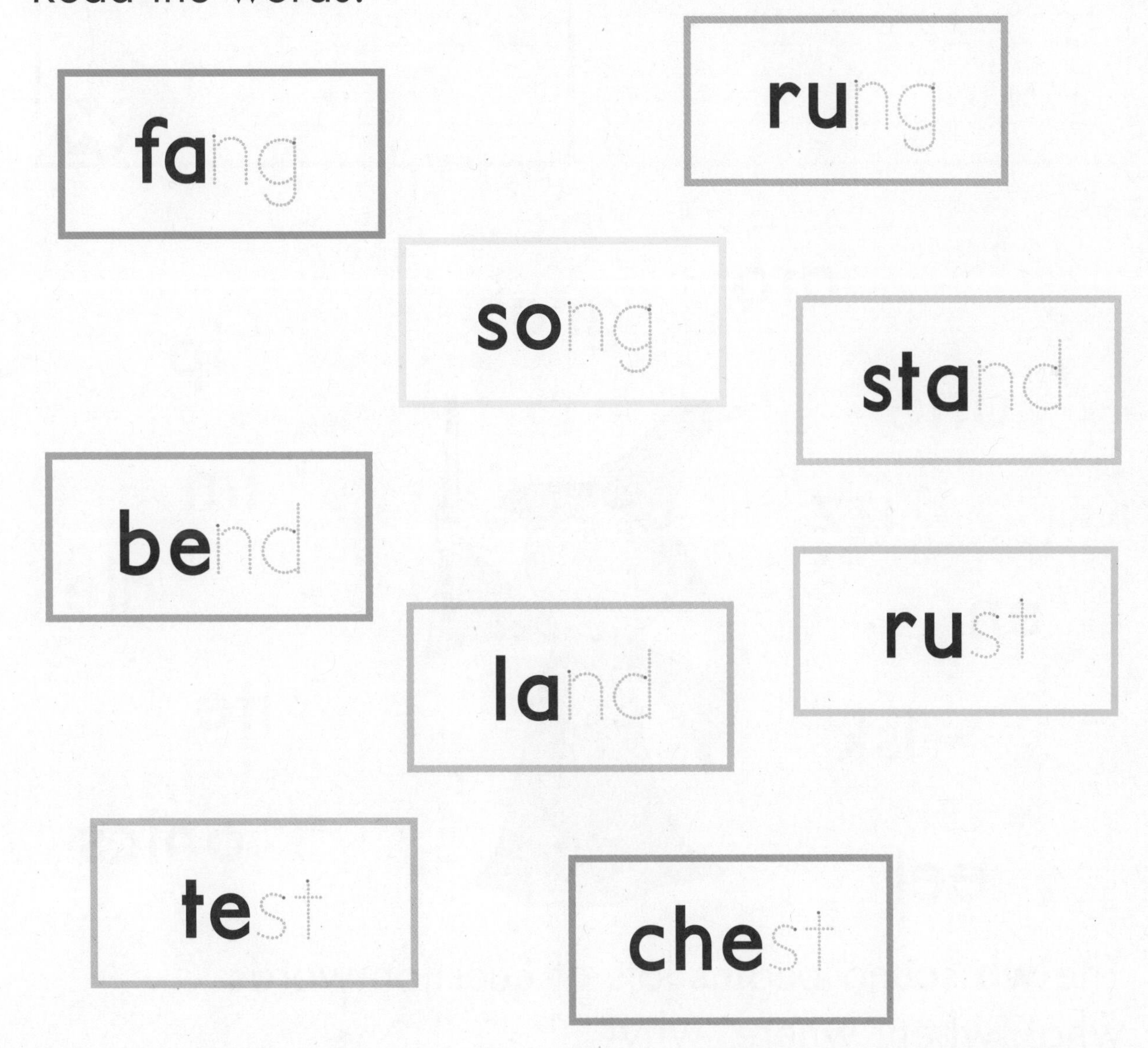

Say the Sounds: wh, ph

Say the sounds of the letters. Trace over the letters.

The **wh** sound begins lots of question words:
what, when, where, why?

Note for parent: Point out that the digraph ph sounds like f.

Silly Words

Blend the letter sounds to read these silly words.

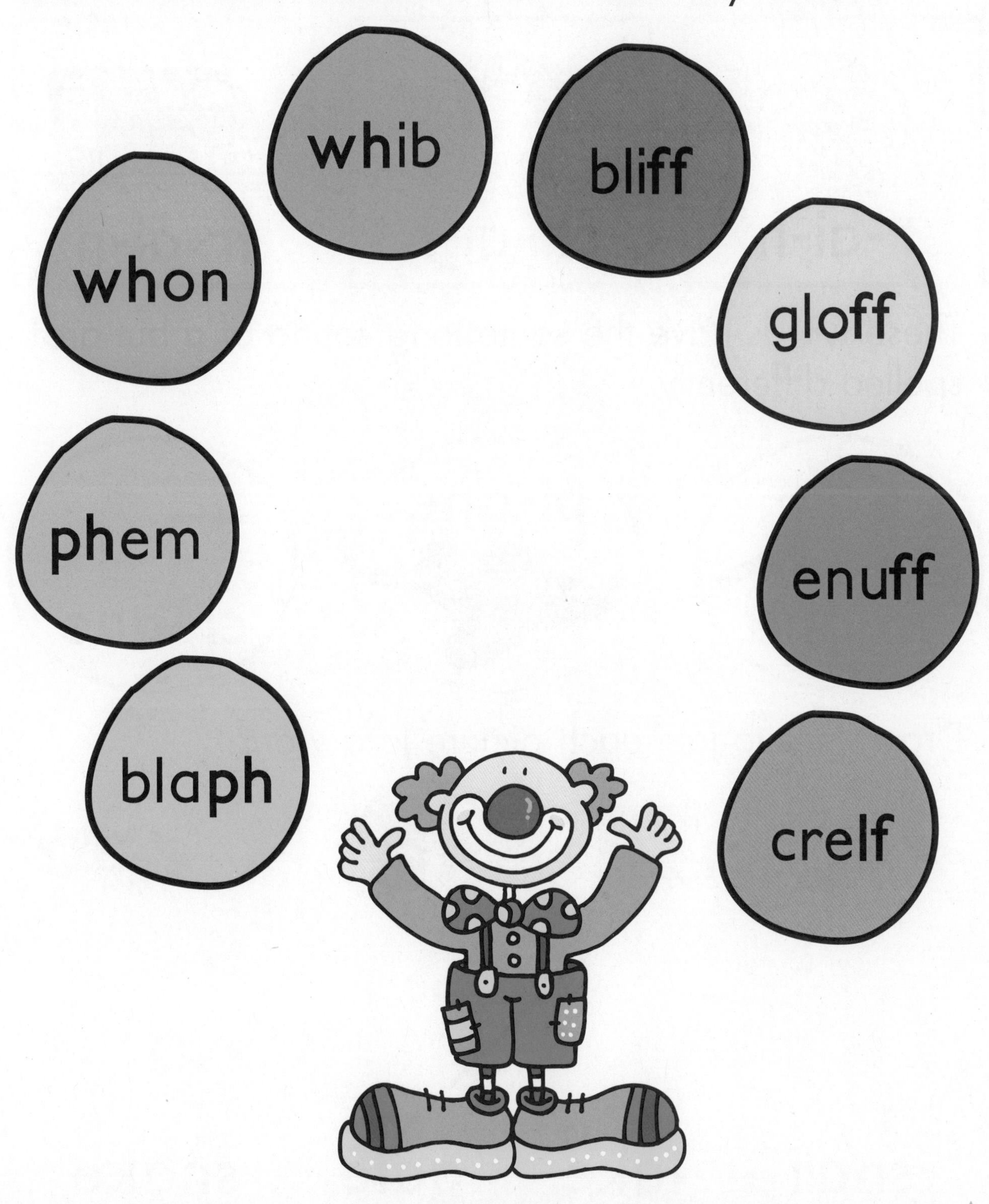

Note for parent: Reading these silly words is a useful test of your child's phonics skills.

Say the Sounds: ai, a-e

Blend the letter sounds **a** and **i** to read these words.

These words have the same long sound of **a** but are spelled differently.

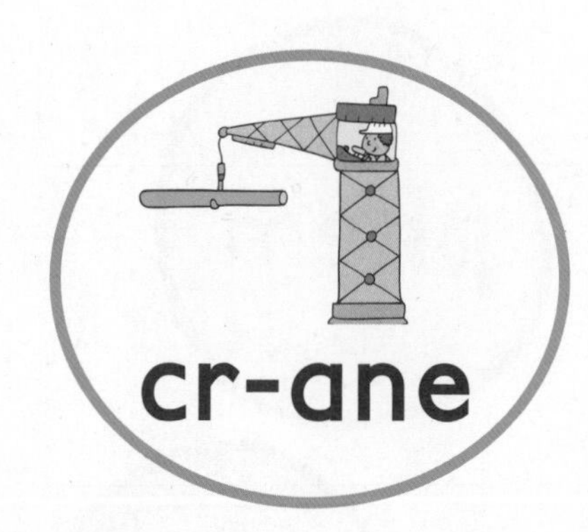

Draw lines to join each picture to a word.

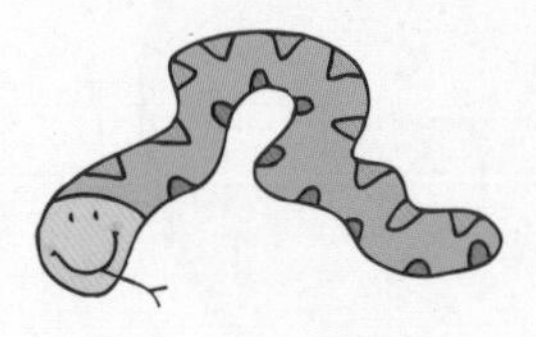

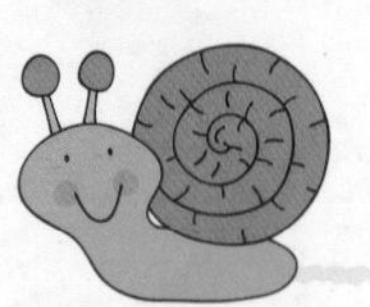

snail **lake** **gate** **snake**

Note for parent: Listen for the long sound of a in these words.

Sounds the Same

Words can sound the same but have different meanings.

For example:

A squirrel has a long **tail**.

This is a fairy-**tale** book.

Circle the words that sound the same but have different meanings.

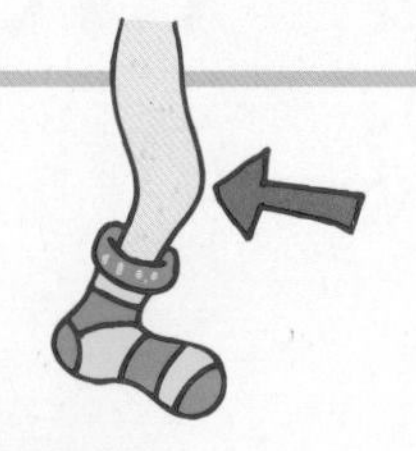

Tim has a **pain** in his knee.

This is a window **pane**.

A town has a **main** street.

A male lion has a **mane**.

Note for parent: Words that sound the same but are spelled differently and have different meanings are called homophones. There are more examples later in the book.

Say the Sound: ay

Trace over the letters.

ay ay ay ay ay

Trace the letters to complete the words.
Read the poem.

Boat in the bay

Pay day

Mouse in the hay

May day

Sun's rays

This way

I say

Let's play!

Note for parent: It is easy to write your own poems in this way by using one rhyming sound and repeating it on every line.

Days of the Week

Trace over the letters to complete the names of the days. Read the poem.

Monday's child is fair of face,
Tuesday's child is full of grace,
Wednesday's child is full of woe,
Thursday's child has far to go,
Friday's child is loving and giving,
Saturday's child works hard for a living,
But the child that was born on
Sunday is happy, smiling, and
has lots to say!

Note for parent: Tell your child the day on which they were born. Do they think the rhyme could be true? Discuss this together.

Say the Sounds: ee, ea

The letter sounds **ee** and **ea** often sound the same.
For example:

I can see a spider.

I can see the sea!

They sound the same but have different meanings.

Say this rhyme.

A sailor went to the sea sea sea,
To see what he could see see see,
But all that he could see see see,
Was the bottom of the
deep blue sea sea sea!

Note for parent: Follow the words with your finger. Point out that see and sea sound the same but are spelled differently.

Nonsense Rhyme

Read this nonsense rhyme. Listen for the sounds **ee** and **ea**. Circle them all. Can you find all five?

There was a young girl called Jean
Who wanted to look like a bean.
She dressed in red and everyone said,
"Beans are meant to be green!"

Draw pictures to match these words.

a cream cake	a neat seat	a dream team
a sheep's feet	a sweet treat	a shark's teeth

Note for parent: ea in meant is a short sound, but in Jean and bean(s) it is a long sound.

Say the Sound: ea (short sound)

Trace over the letters.

ea ea ea ea ea

Write the letters **ea** in the spaces to complete the words. Read the words.

sleepy h_ _d

brown br_ _d

light as a f_ _ther

blue thr_ _d

winter w_ _ther

green m_ _dow

Draw the missing pictures to match the words.

Note for parent: Compare the short sound of ea in head with the long sound of ea in cream.

Say the Sound: i-e

The **e** at the end of these words changes **i** from a short sound into a long sound.

Say these words:

pin – pine	**bit – bite**

Write **e** at the end of the words then read them aloud.

spin_
ric_
slic_
mik_
ic_
bik_
lik_
hik_
nic_
trik_

Note for parent: Sometimes the e at the end of these words is called magic e because it changes the sound of the vowel that comes before it.

Magic e

Write e at the end of these words to make new words.

Note for parent: Here are more examples of magic e.

Say the Sounds: igh, y

Trace over the letters.

igh **as in night**

y **as in sky**

Trace the letters to complete the words.
Blend the sounds to read the words.

Note for parent: Listen for the long igh or y sound in these words.

Read the Poem

Write the letters **ight** in the spaces to complete the words in the poem.

Fright Night!

Late last n _ _ _ _,

I had a fr _ _ _ _,

I turned on the l _ _ _ _,

The sky was br_ _ _ _,

I pulled the covers t _ _ _ _,

And hid from s _ _ _ _,

Thunder and l _ _ _ _ ning

Is so fr _ _ _ _ ening!

Then out came the morning sun

With golden boxing gloves on,

The sun won the f _ _ _ _,

Everything was all r _ _ _ _.

Note for parent: It is easy to write your own poems in this way by using one rhyming sound and repeating it on every line.

Answer the Questions

Read the questions. Circle **yes** or **no**.

Can a duck read?  yes no

Can a dog cry? yes no 

Can a cat play bingo?  yes no

Can gelatin wobble? yes no  

Can you ride a bike?  yes no

Can you say a rhyme? yes no 

Can ice melt? 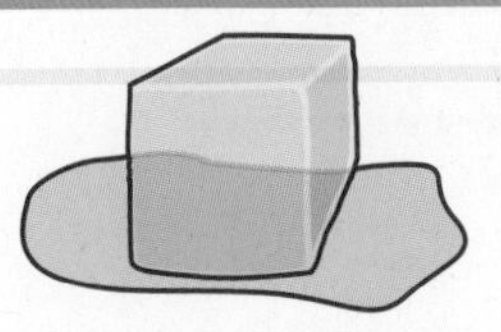 yes no

Can the sun freeze?  yes no

Note for parent: Together you can make up some more questions and try them out on family and friends.

Say the Sound: ow, oa

Trace over the letters to write the sounds in the words. Read the captions. Draw the missing pictures.

billy goat

long coat

warty toad

rowing boat

deep snow

dog show

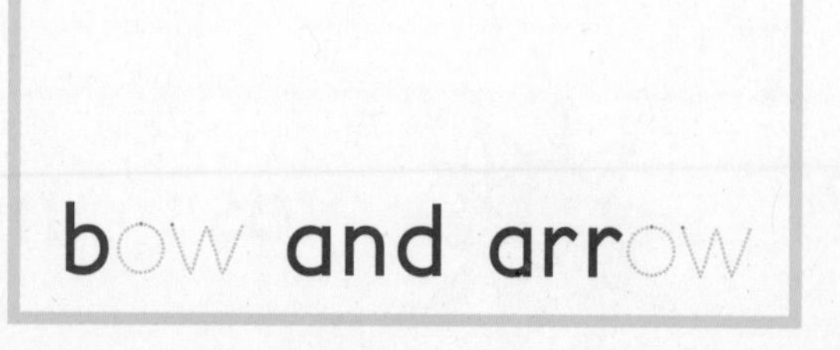

bow and arrow

flower growing

Note for parent: Notice flower is a different ow sound.

Say the Sound: oa, o-e

Read the words on the stones. Find a path across the river by coloring in words that rhyme with **stone**.

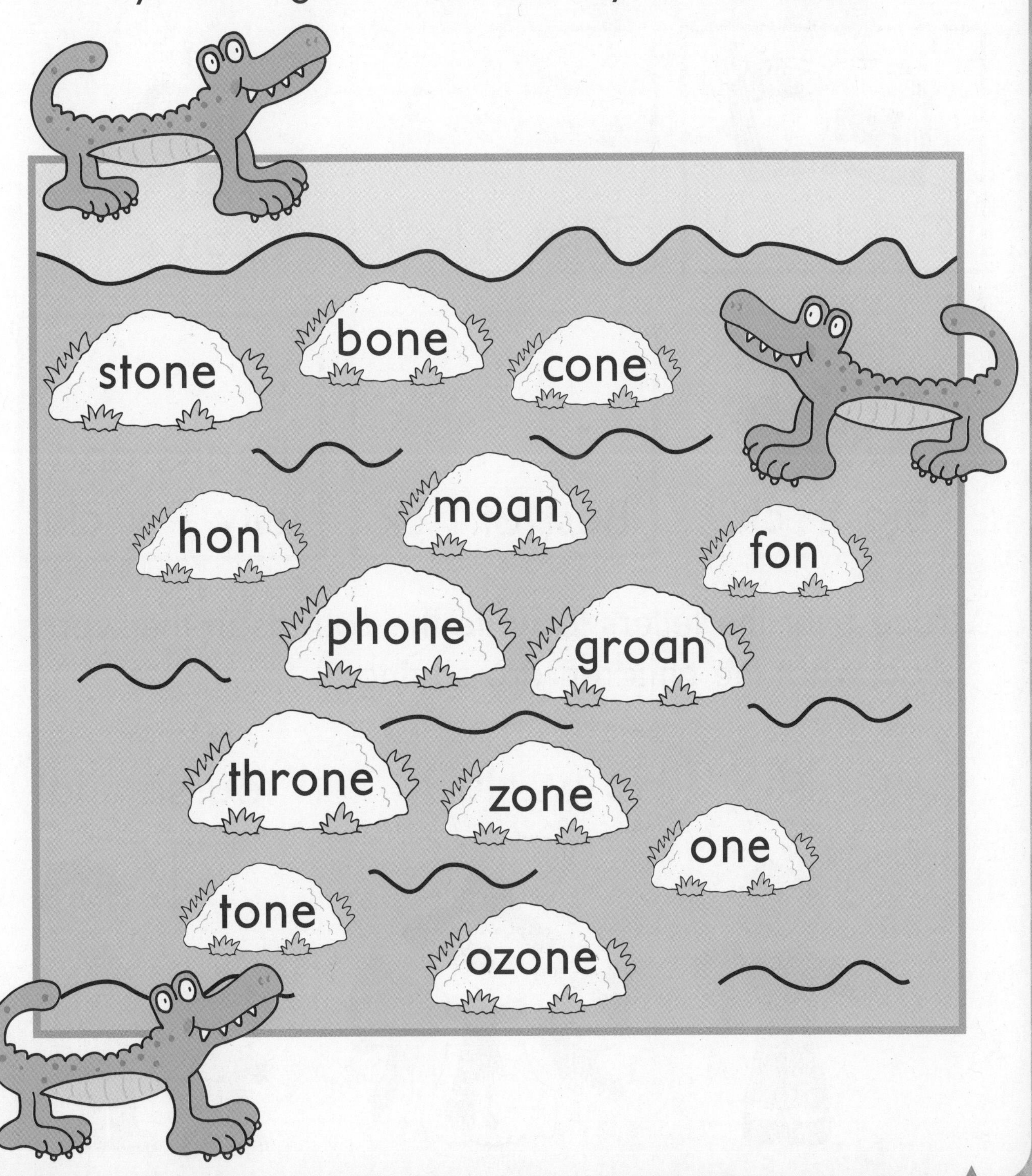

Note for parent: Some of these words are nonsense or silly words, i.e., fon, hon – they don't rhyme with stone. However, moan and groan do rhyme.

Say the Sounds: oo, ou, u

Trace over the letters to write the sounds in the words. Read the captions. Draw the missing pictures.

Good book

Take a look

I can cook

Big truck

Best of luck

Beans and jelly – yuck!

Trace over the letters to write the sounds in the words. Read what the children are saying.

Note for parent: The pronunciation of words such as book will vary due to different regional accents.

Different Books

Read the names of these different types of books. Tick the ones that you have at home.

cookbook ☐

workbook ☐

sketchbook ☐

scrapbook ☐

textbook ☐

notebook ☐

storybook ☐

handbook ☐

Note for parent: Identify these types of books. Look at examples if you have them at home.

Say the Sounds: ar, or

Read the words. Listen for the different sounds of **ar** and **or** in these words.

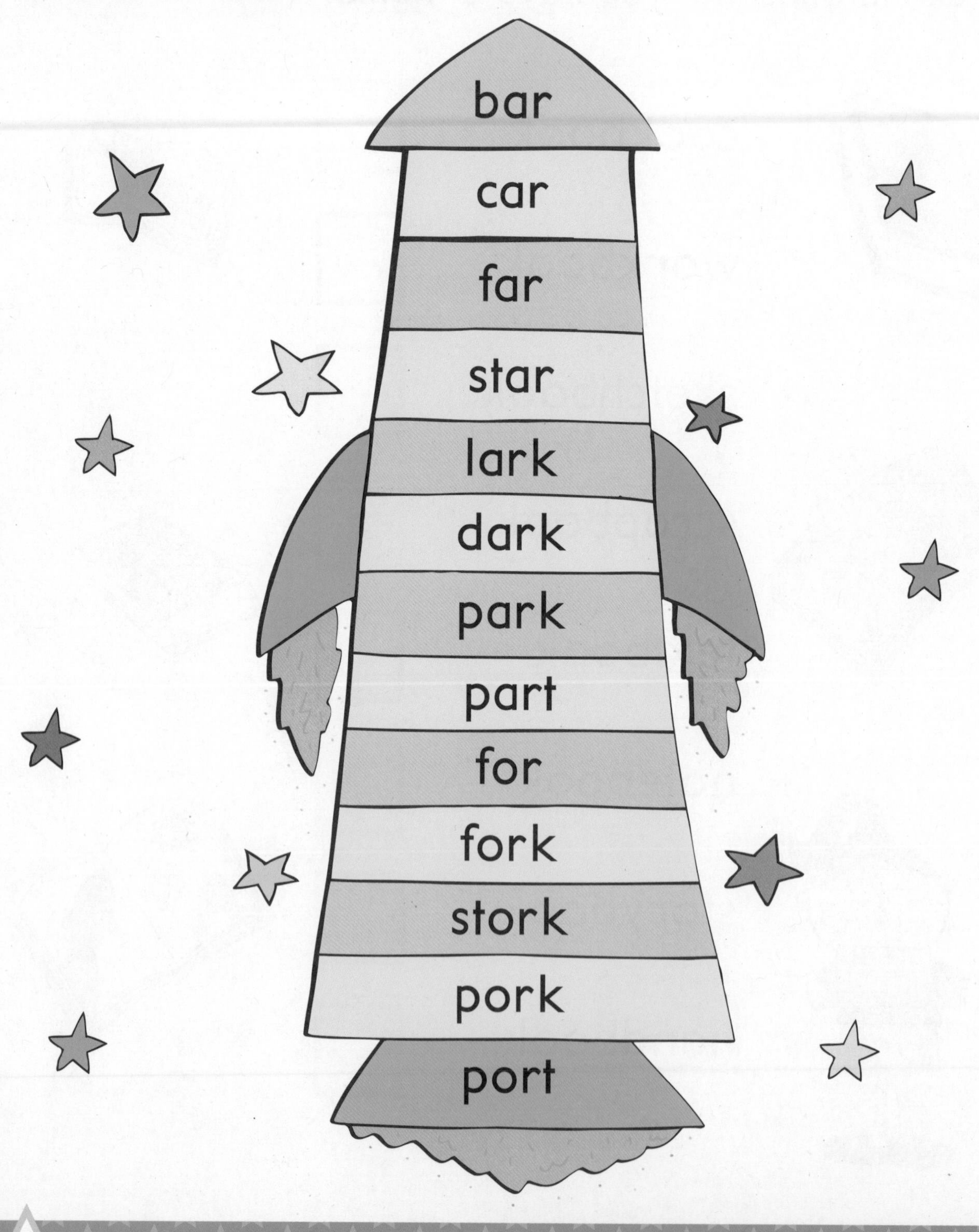

Note for parents: Help your child to read these words. Follow the words with your finger. Listen for the differences.

Say the Sounds: ore, oor, oar, aw

Write the missing letters to make these words.

core score store shore floor door

front d_ _ _

apple c_ _ _

clean fl_ _ _

food st_ _ _

sea sh_ _ _

big sc_ _ _

Write **oar** and **aw** in these words:

Wild b_ _ _ and lion's r_ _ _!

Dog's p_ _ and shark's j_ _!

Note for parent: Point out that these letter endings look different but they sound the same, though in some regional accents they may differ.

Tricky Words

Read and try to remember what these tricky words look like.

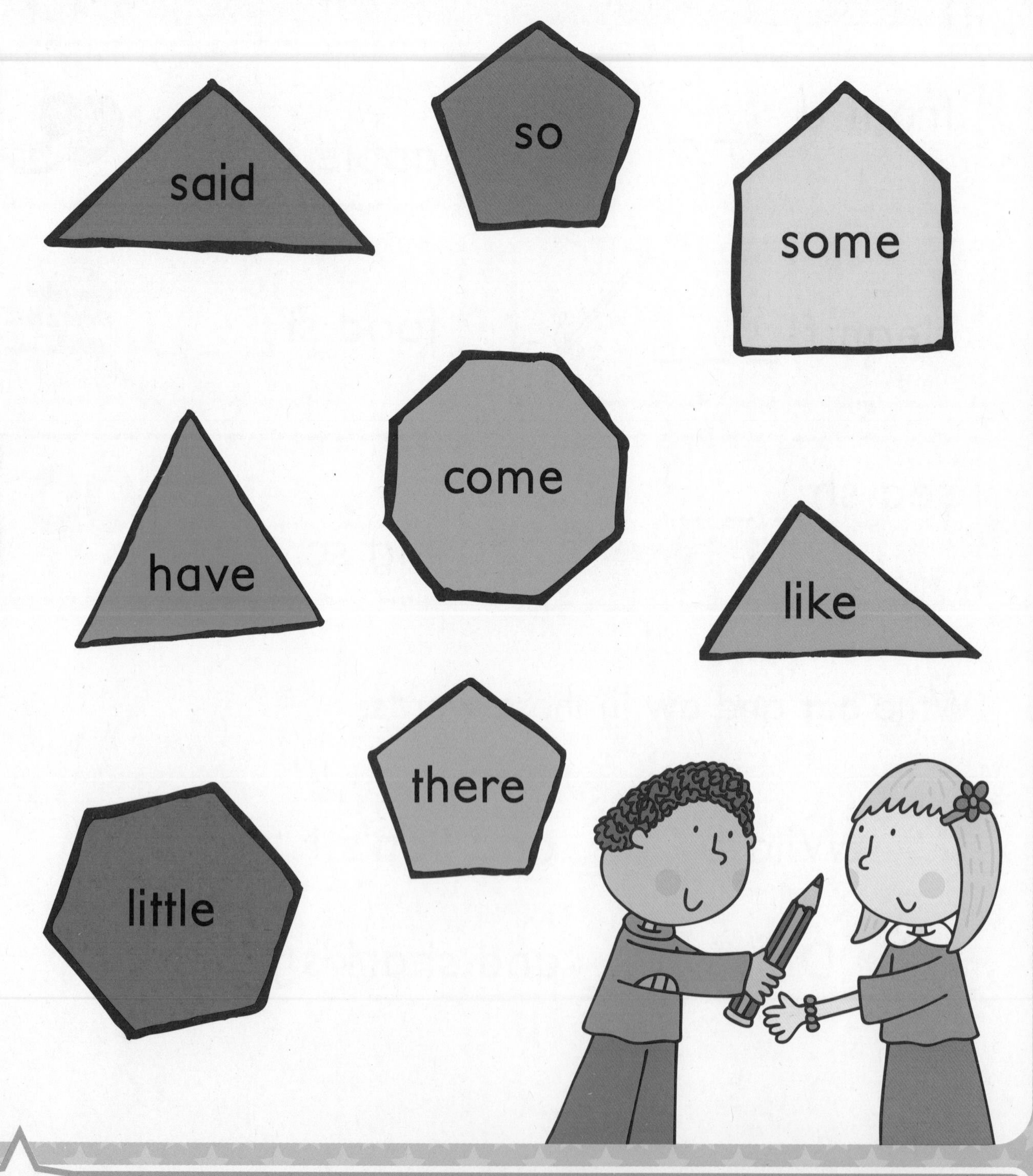

Note for parent: There is no easy way of learning these words. But with practice and familiarity your child will begin to recognize them on sight.

Tricky Test

Which is correct? Circle the correct word.

sed or said

soe or so

some or som

com or come

hav or have

like or lyke

littel or little

there or thare

Say the Sounds: ear, air, a-e

Draw lines to join the words that sound the same.

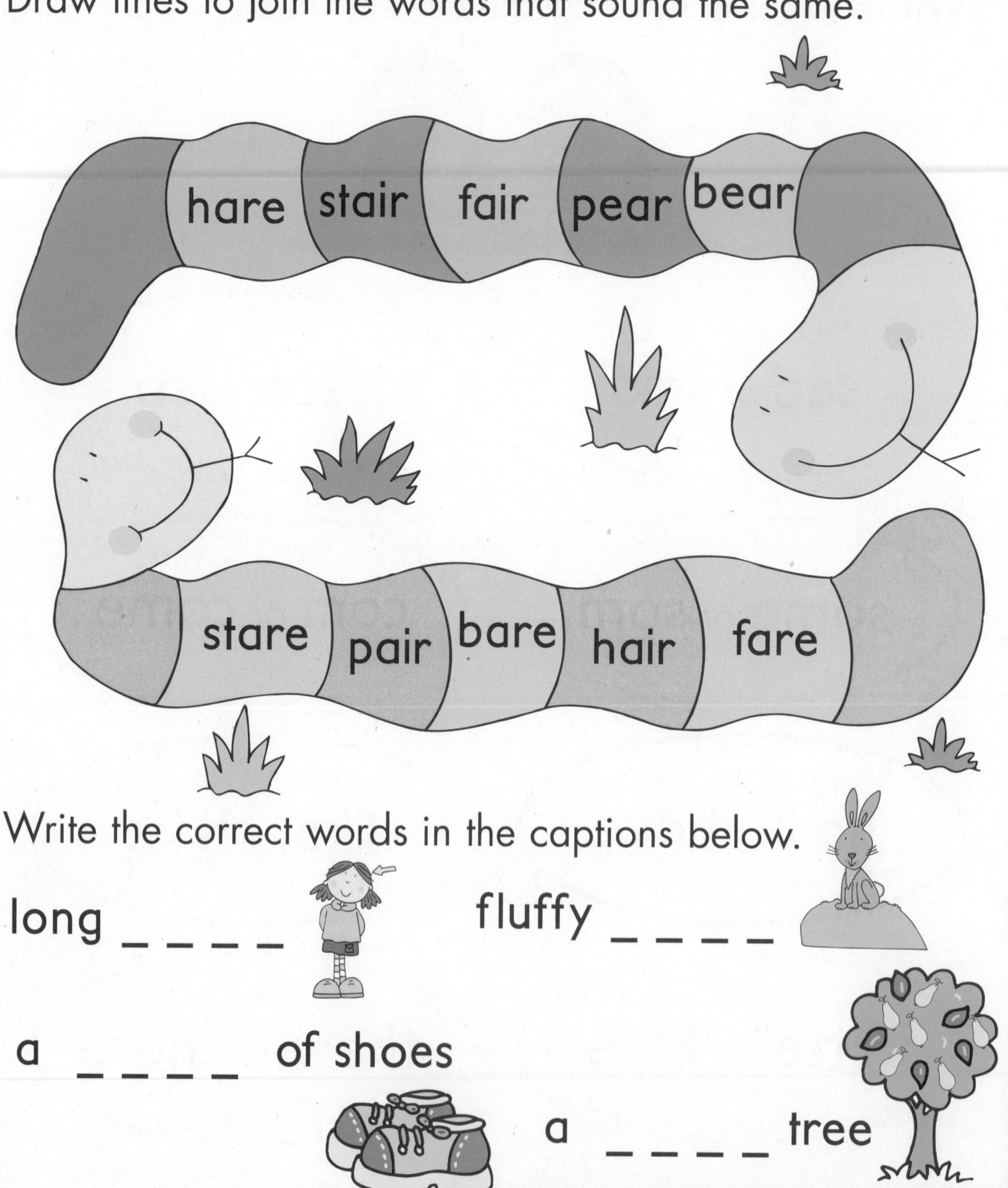

Write the correct words in the captions below.

long _ _ _ _

fluffy _ _ _ _

a _ _ _ _ of shoes

a _ _ _ _ tree

Note for parent: Words such as fare, hare, and stare are sometimes called magic e words because the final e changes the sound of the vowel that comes before it.

Match the Definitions

Choose the correct word to match each definition.
Copy the word into the space.

mare
square
footwear
high chair
nightmare
swimwear

A four-sided shape ____________

A chair for babies ____________

A female horse ____________

A bad dream ____________

Clothes for swimming ____________

Boots, shoes, and sandals ____________

Note for parent: The endings mare, wear, and air are rhyming in these words.

Say the Sound: er

Draw lines to join the labels to the people in the photograph. Who do you think they are?

Choose from the following words:

mother	father	brother
sister	grandfather	grandmother

Note for parents: These common words are useful to learn.

Compound Words

Some words are made by joining two words together.
Draw lines to join two words to make a new word.

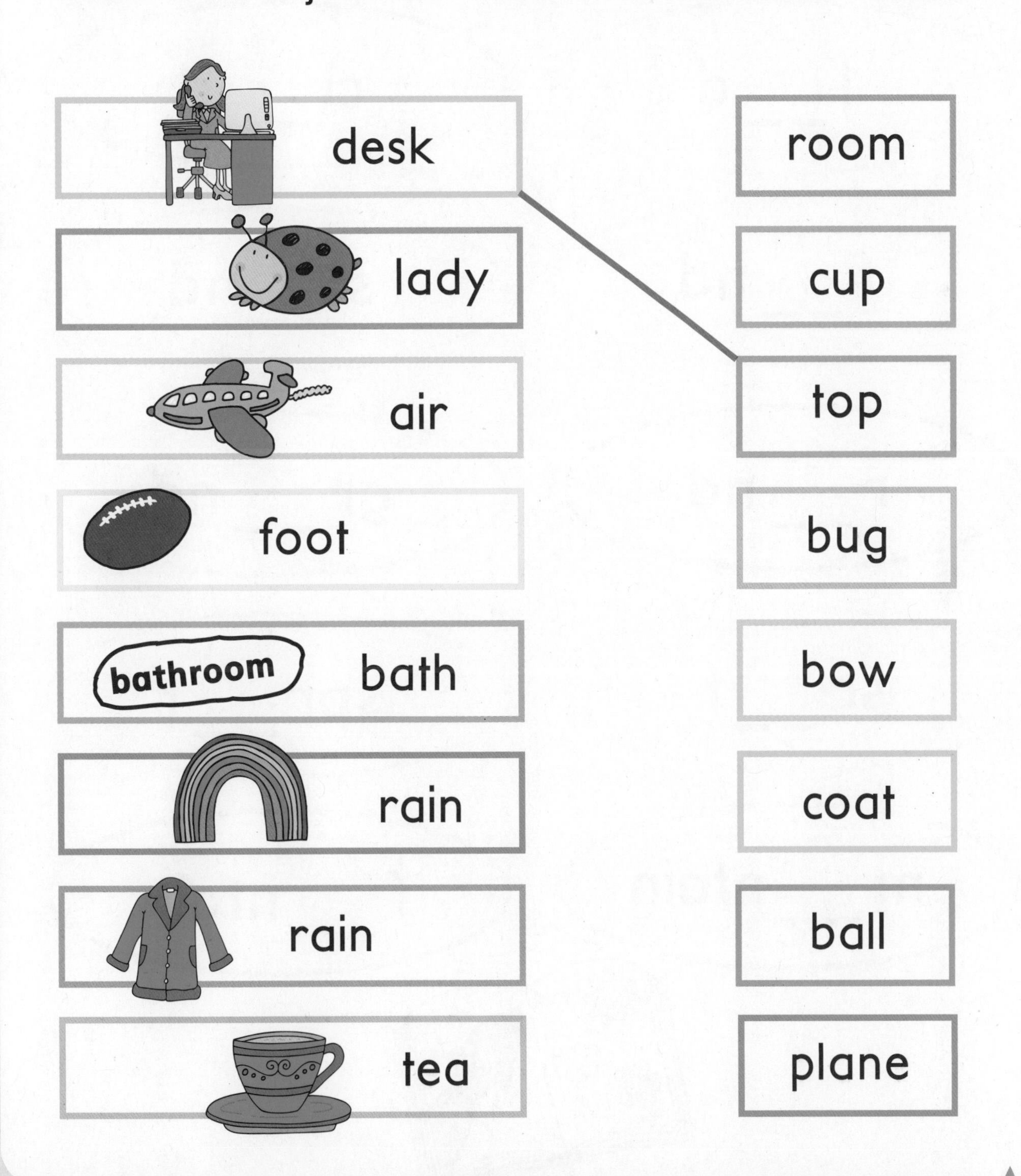

Say the Sound: ou

Write the **ou** sounds in the words. Read the words.

l __ __ d

cl __ __ d

f __ __ nd

s __ __ nd

r __ __ nd

gr __ __ nd

sc __ __ t

spr __ __ t

m __ __ ntain

f __ __ ntain

Note for parent: These are examples of the long sound of ou. Compare them with ou in could on page 68, which is a short sound.

What Is . . . ?

Read each question and choose a word from the list below. Write the word on the line.

cloud	round	sprout
fountain	ground	found

What is green all over and good for you? ____________________

What is white, gray, or black and floats above you? ____________________

What is the opposite of lost? ____________________

What is wet and watery and goes up and down? ____________________

What is under your feet? ____________________

What is a ball shape? ____________________

Note for parent: Help your child to think of words that use the short sound for ou such as would.

Say the Sound: oi, oy

Trace over the letters.

oi oy

Trace the letters to complete the words.
Read the words.

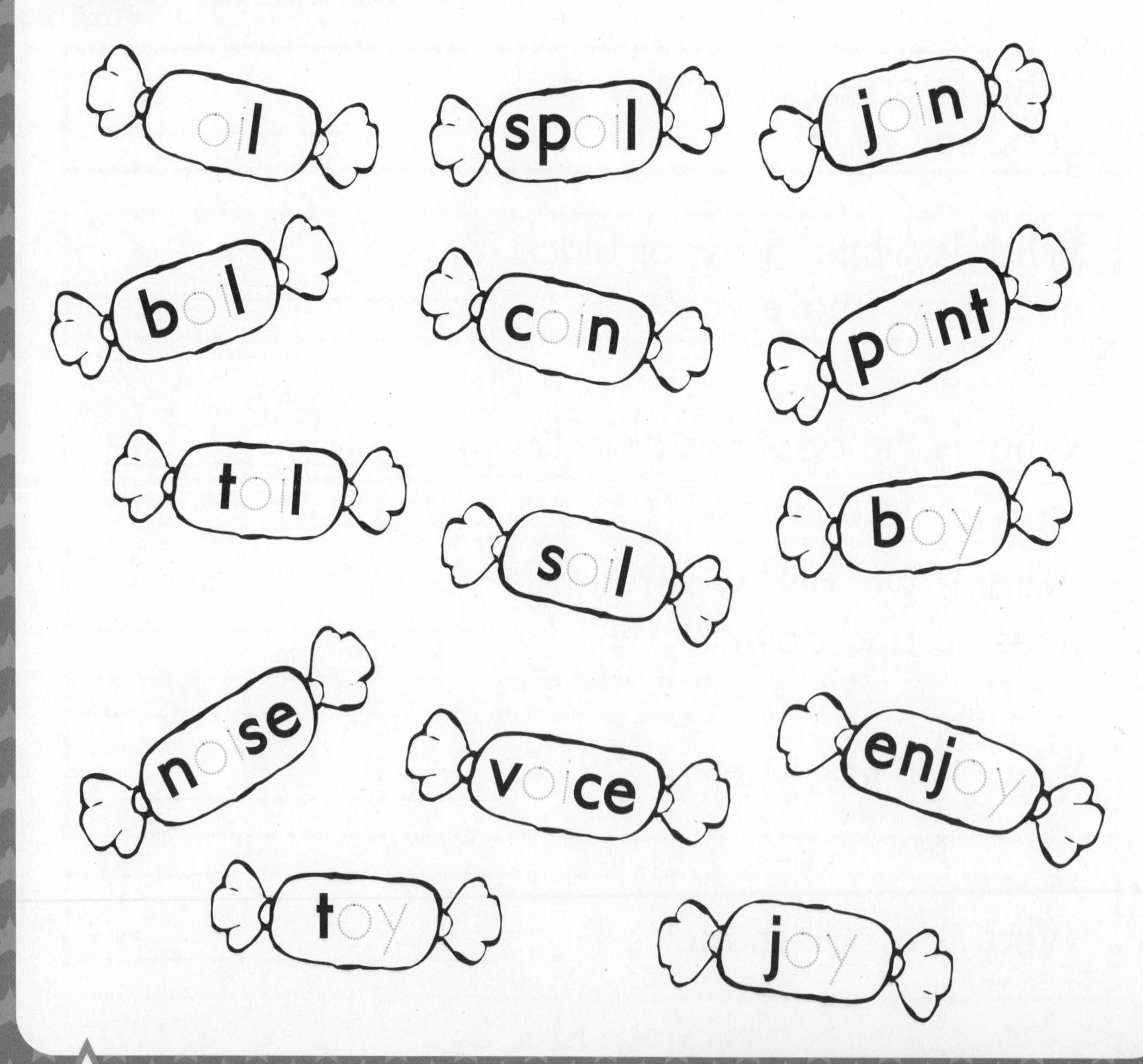

Note for parent: Here o comes before i. Compare with kiosk, which is a different sound.

Match the Definitions

Choose a word to fit each definition.
Write it in the space.

boil soil spoil coin voice oil join

You might put this in your car. ____________

You do this to water to make it hot. ____________

You plant seeds in this. ____________

You use this to pay for things. ____________

You ruin something. ____________

You put things together. ____________

You use this to speak. ____________

Note for parent: Encourage your child to check their spellings.

Tricky Words

Read and try to remember what these tricky words look like.

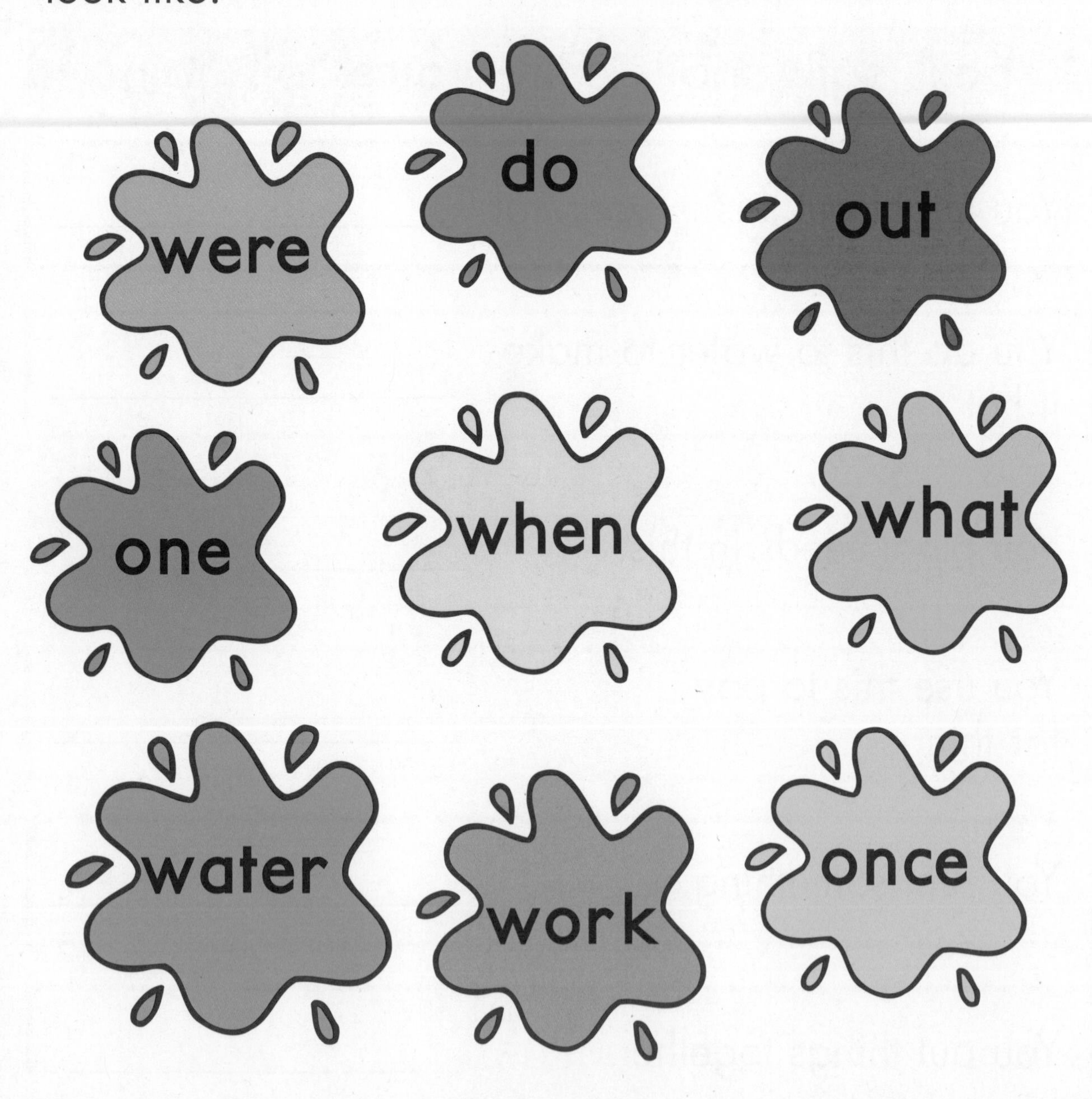

You can test how well you have remembered them on the opposite page. First, you must cover this page.

Note for parent: There is no easy way of learning these words. But with practice and familiarity your child will begin to recognize them on sight.

Tricky Test

Which is correct? Circle the correct word.

were or weur

duw or do

owt or out

wone or one

wen or when

whot or what

water or worter

werk or work

wonce or once

Say the Sounds: ew, ue, oo, u-e

Read the words to hear the ew, ue, oo, and u-e sounds.

Note for parent: These are long vowel sounds.

Find the Rhyme

Draw lines to join words that rhyme.

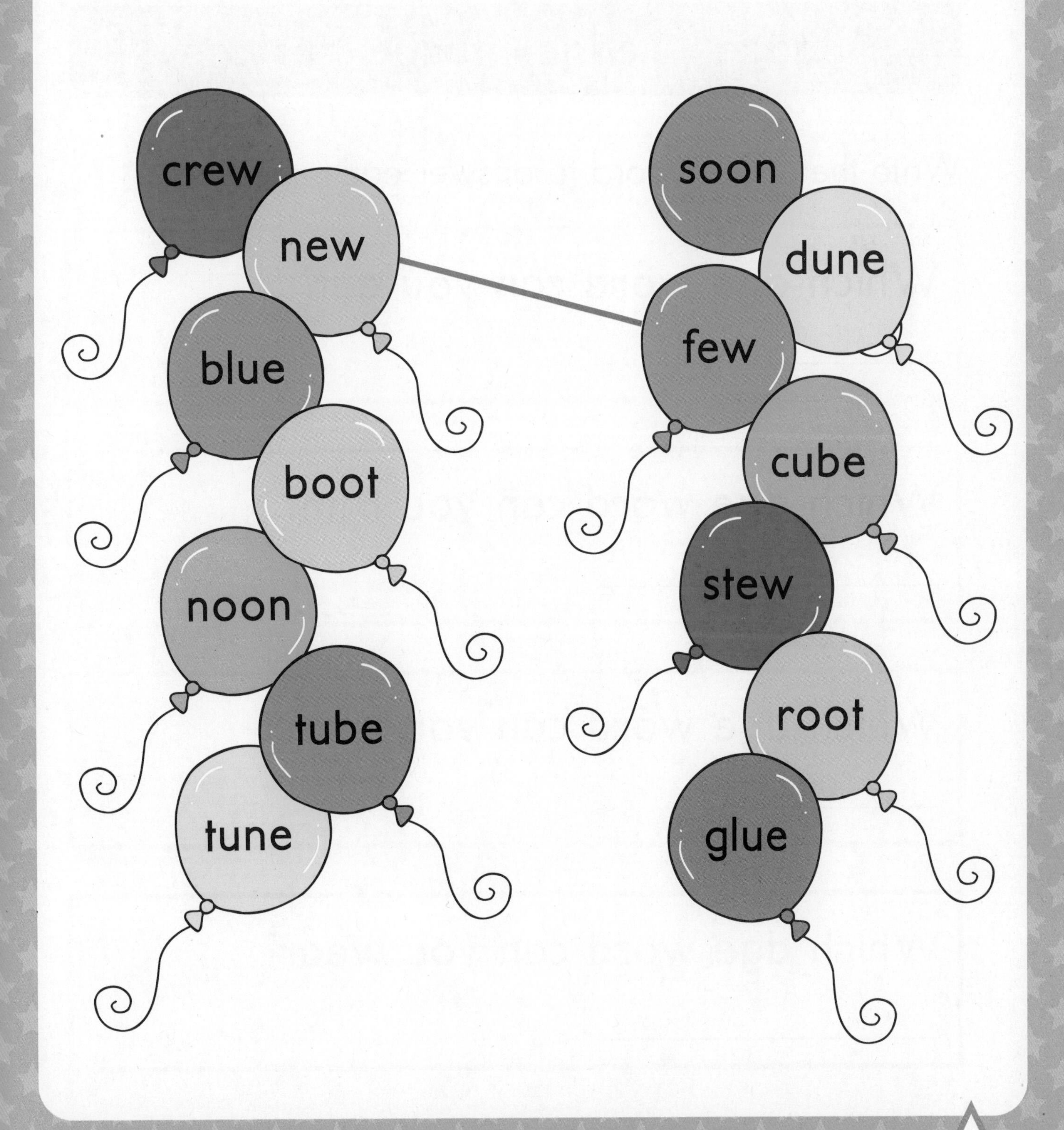

Note for parent: Emphasize the ends of the words as you read them.

Say the Sound: dge

Read the words below.

badge hedge fudge bridge

Write the correct word to answer each question.

Which **dge** word can you eat?

____

Which **dge** word can you trim?

____

Which **dge** word can you cross?

____

Which **dge** word can you wear?

____

Note for parent: These three letters are called a consonant trigraph. Together they make one sound.

Sound Story: g, t

Read the story. Listen for the sounds of **g** and **t**.

One day a huge giant met a tall giraffe.
"I am the tallest creature in the land!" said the giant.
"I can touch the sky if I want to!"
"You are not taller than me!" said the giraffe.
"I can touch the tops of the trees with my tongue!"
"I can do that, too!" said the giant.
Just then a tiny ant scuttled at their feet.
"I can touch the top of that mountain," said the ant.
The huge giant and the tall giraffe both laughed.
"No you can't!" they said.
Then the tiny ant ran up the mountain to the very top!
"Told you so!" said the tiny ant.

Note for parent: Read the story together. Follow the words with your finger and emphasize the sounds g and t. Notice that giraffe and giant have the same sound.

Say the Sound: le

Read the words. Choose a word to fit each definition. Write it in the space.

little bottle kettle settle
nettle rattle cattle

You boil water in it. ________

You can get a red rash from it. ________

Provide us with milk and meat. ________

Not big. ________

It holds liquid. ________

Baby's noisy toy. ________

Note for parent: The double t sound is commonly followed by le.

Hey, Diddle, Diddle

Say the nursery rhyme.

Hey, diddle, diddle,
The cat and the fiddle,
The cow jumped over the moon.
The little dog laughed to see such fun,
And the dish ran away with the spoon!

Trace over the letters to complete the words.
Read the words.

middle riddle toddle muddle

huddle cuddle puddle paddle

Note for parent: Teach your child some well-known nursery rhymes. The language patterns found within them are a good literacy tool.

Read the Rhyme

Say the rhyme. Listen for repeated sounds.

Hubble, bubble,
Toil and trouble,
Fire burn and cauldron bubble!

Now read the words in the cauldron. Some are silly words!

Note for parent: Reading silly words is a good test of your child's phonics skills.

Rhyming Wheel

Draw lines to join words that rhyme with the word in the middle of the wheel.

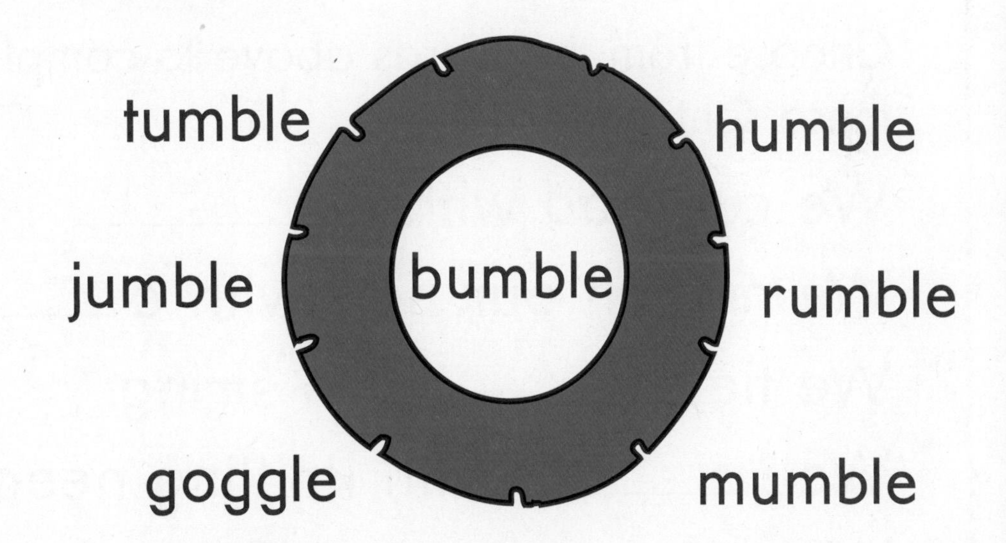

Which words do not rhyme?

Write them here: ______________________________

Note for parent: Discuss why gaggle and goggle don't rhyme with the other words in the wheels.

Silent Letters: b, k

Some words have silent letters that are not pronounced when we say the word.

For example:
lamb has a silent **b**  knight has a silent **k**

Trace over the silent letters in these words.
Say the words.

comb thumb knife know knit

knot knee kneel knock knuckle

Choose from the words above to complete these sentences.

We cut food with a __________.

We neaten our hair with a __________.

We tie a __________ in string.

We __________ with knitting needles.

We __________ and understand.

We __________ on our knees.

We __________ on the door.

Note for parent: Together think of more silent letter words.

Silent Letters: g, w

Trace over the silent letters in these words.
Say the words.

gnaw gnome gnat write wrist
wrong wrap wreck wrestle wriggle

Join the words to the definition.

A garden ornament	gnaw
A small biting insect	wrong
A join in the arm	write
Not right	gnat
To make words	gnome
To bite and chew	wrist

Note for parent: Together think of more silent letter words.

Say the Sound: y Ending

Trace over the **y** endings to complete the words.
Read the words.

hairy scary happy
bony funny sunny

Choose a word from the list above to fit each caption. Write the word in the space.

A __________ day

A __________ birthday

A __________ clown

A __________ goat

A __________ skeleton

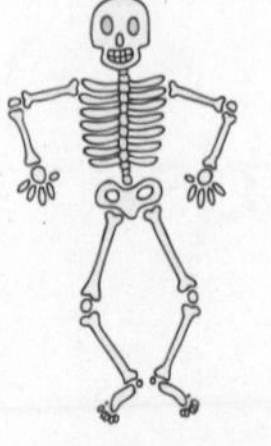

A __________ monster

Note for parent: Older children may know that describing words such as these are called adjectives.

More y Endings

Trace over the **y** endings to complete the words.
Read the words.

mommy dadd y bab y
pupp y fair y bunn y

Choose a word from the list above to finish each caption. Write the word in the space.

A happy __________

A messy __________

A silly __________

A busy __________

A pretty __________

A fluffy __________

Note for parent: Think of alternative adjectives for these pictures.

Sounding and Blending

Sound out the letters. Then blend the sounds to read the words

For example: **dr-i-nk**

Note for parent: If the word doesn't "sound right," encourage your child to try again or suggest what the word might be.

Silly Sounds

Try these silly sounds. Blend them together to read the words.

bl-u-nk

tw-u-st

fr-i-nt

fl-e-nd

gr-e-nt

dr-o-st

cr-a-nd

sw-i-sk

Tricky Words

Read and try to remember what these tricky words look like.

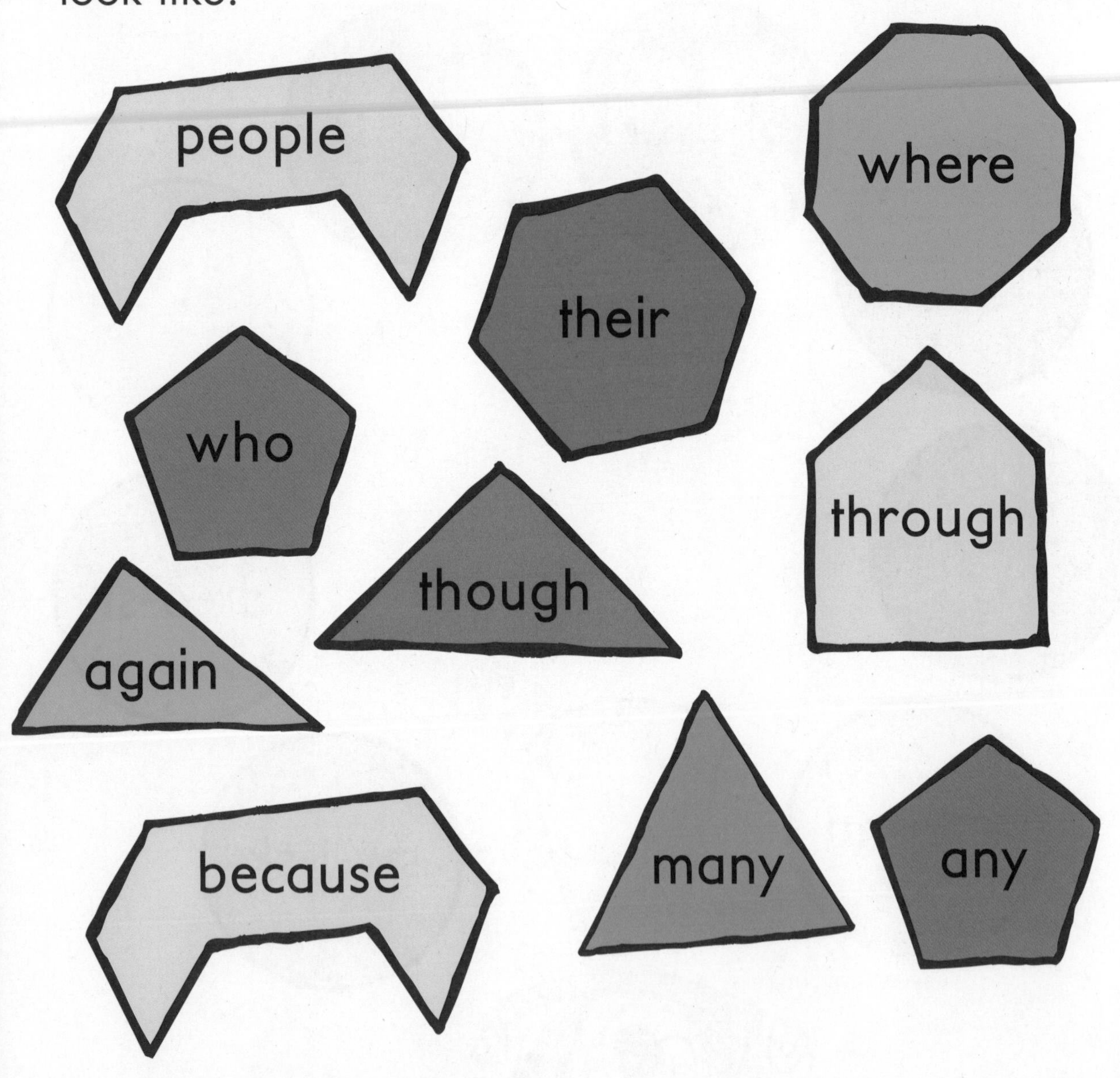

You can test how well you have remembered them on the opposite page. First, you must cover this page.

Note for parent: There is no easy way of learning these words. But with practice and familiarity your child will begin to recognize them on sight.

Tricky Test

Which is correct? Circle the correct word.

peeple or people

thair or their

where or weer

who or whu

agen or again

thow or though

thruw or through

meny or many

becus or because

any or eny

Note for parent: This activity will support your child in identifying tricky words.

Say the Sound: tch

Trace over the sounds to complete these words.
Draw the missing pictures.

catch

match

watch

fetch

witch

switch

hutch

hatch

itchy

kitchen

Note for parents: tch is a consonant trigraph. Try to think of further examples of this trigraph to add to the list.

Blending Two Halves

Blend the two halves of each word together. Say the word, then write it in the space.

spr - int	sprint
str - ing	
str - ong	
str - eam	
str - eet	
scr - ew	
scr - ape	
scr - eam	
shr - imp	
sti - tch	

Note for parent: At this stage, we can split these words neatly into two halves to aid blending.

Read the Signs

Complete the signs. Write the missing letters in the spaces.

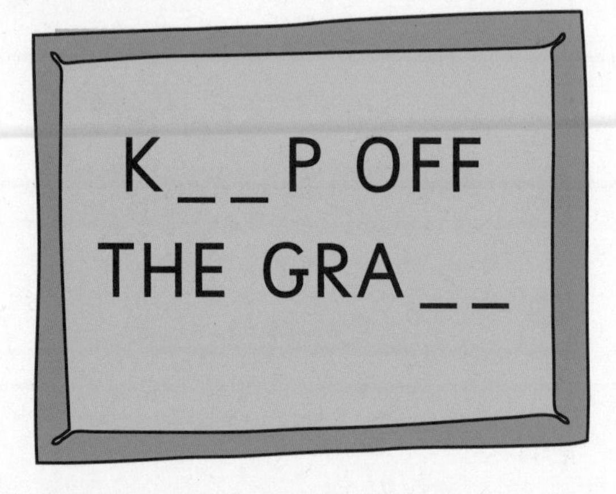

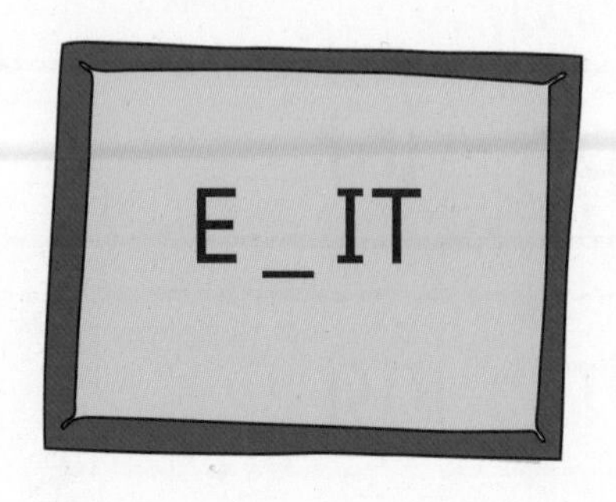

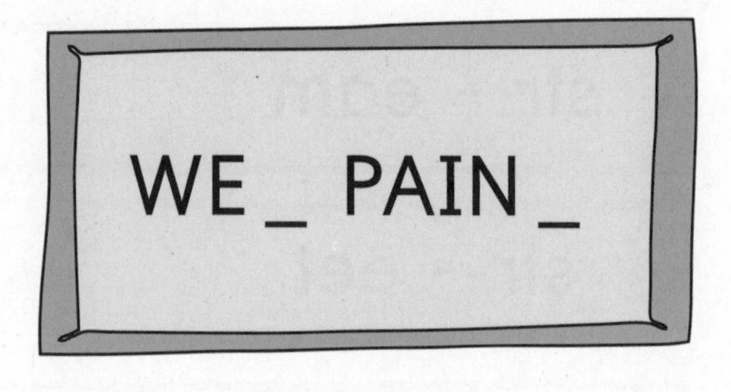

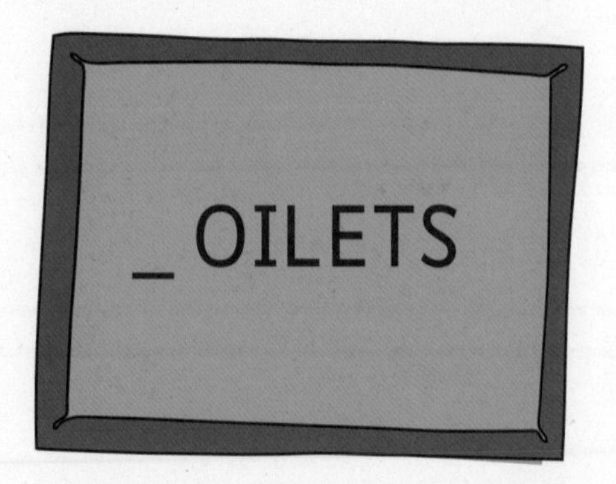

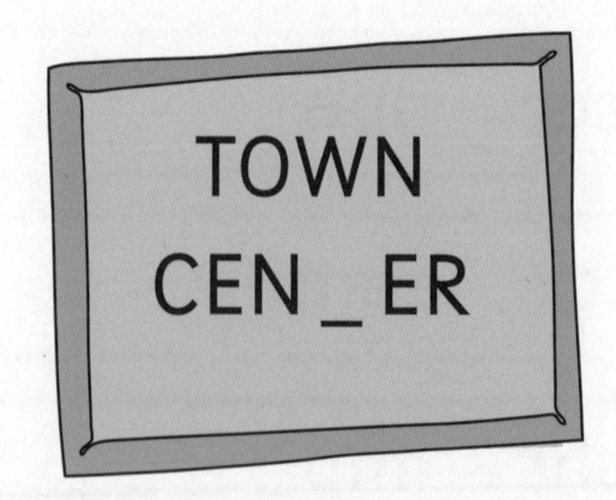

K _ _ P OFF
THE GRA _ _

E _ IT

D _ NGER
KEEP OU _!

WE _ PAIN _

_ OILETS

TOWN
CEN _ ER

Note for parent: Read road and street signs when you are out and about together.

Silly Signs

Read the silly signs from Ugland. Can you spot the spelling mistakes? Write the correct spellings underneath.

WELCOM TO UGLAND

____

UM'S HOWSE

____

RIVAR UG

____

UG MUG'S TEE SHOP

____

KAR WASH

____

UGLAND ERRPORT

____

Note for parent: Have fun figuring out what the signs should say!

Say the Sound: tion

Blend the sounds. Say the words.

sta-tion	station
cap-tion	caption
rel-a-tion	relation
loc-a-tion	location
edu-ca-tion	education
imag-in-a-tion	imagination
exam-in-a-tion	examination

Choose a word above to complete each sentence.

The train arrives at the ______________ .

My school gives me an ______________ .

I use my ______________ when I write a story.

Members of my family are my ______________s.

Note for parent: Discuss the meanings of these words and give examples.

Say the Sound: ture

Blend the sounds to read the words on the book covers.

Which type of book do you like best?
Write the title in the space below.

___

Plurals

When there is more than one of something, it is called a plural.

For example: **kittens**

Make these words plural by writing **s** at the end.

dog_	hat_
flower_	star_
tree_	chair_
book_	umbrella_

But… if a word ends in **ch**, **sh**, **s** or **x** we add **es**.
Add es to these words.

watch_ _	box_ _
dish_ _	glass_ _
patch_ _	splash_ _
fox_ _	kiss_ _

Note for parent: Some words don't change in the plural, e.g., sheep, deer. The plural for fish can be fish or fishes – both are acceptable.

More Plurals

If a word ends in **y**, the plural ending becomes **ies**.

For example: baby babies

Add ies to complete these plural words.

fairy fair_ _ _

pony pon_ _ _

bunny bunn_ _ _

Some words end in ves in the plural.

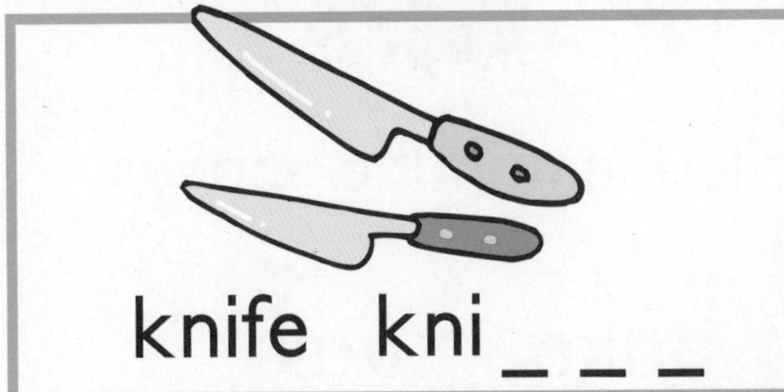

knife kni_ _ _

wife wi_ _ _

life li_ _ _

Note for parent: Discuss other exception words that your child might know, (e.g., foot – feet, tooth – teeth).

Verbs: ing Endings

When a verb ends in **ing** it tells us that the action is happening now.

For example: fly → fly**ing**

Add ing to these words. Write them in the spaces.

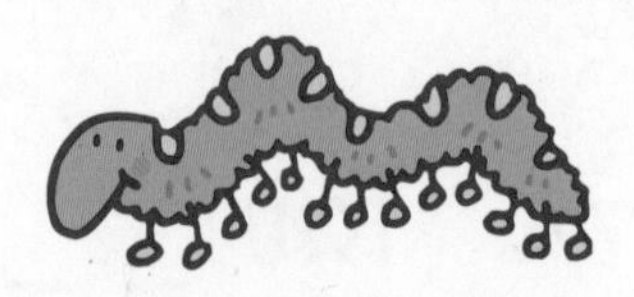

eat _ _ _ jump _ _ _ crawl _ _ _

But… if a word ends in **e**, we drop the e before adding **ing**.

For example: dive → div**ing**

Add ing to these words. Write them in the spaces.

dance	danc _ _ _	bake	bak _ _ _
race	rac _ _ _	ride	rid _ _ _
skate	skat _ _ _	wave	wav _ _ _
		write	writ _ _ _

Note for parent: Explain to your child that a verb is an action or "doing" word.

More ing Endings

If a word has a vowel before the final consonant, we double the consonant before adding **ing**.

For example: run → runn**ing**

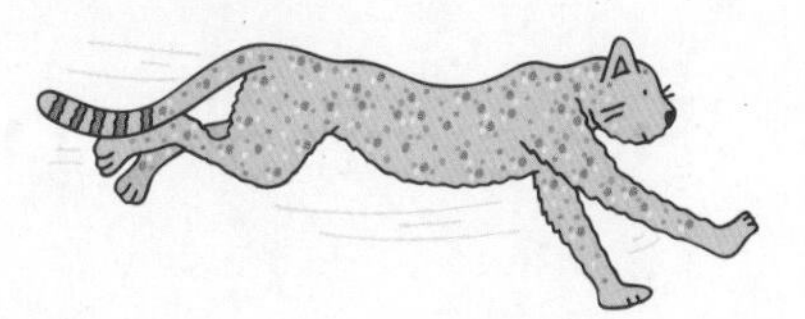

Double the consonant and add **ing** to these words. Write in the spaces.

skip _____

hop _____

swim _____

dig _____

cut _____

clap _____

drip _____

drum _____

Note for parent: Think of more examples that follow this rule in the simple present tense.

Verbs: ed Endings

When a verb ends in **ed** it tells us that the action happened in the past.

For example: play → play**ed**

Add ed to these words. Write them in the spaces.

walk _ _   look _ _   cook _ _

push _ _   pull _ _   help _ _

Double the consonant and add ed to these words.

skip _ _ _   shop _ _ _

Note for parent: Think of more examples of past tense verbs ending in ed.

Exception Words

Some past tense verbs don't follow the rules.
Read them and learn to spell them.

Note for parent: Learn to spell these words by first looking at them, then covering them, then writing them out and, finally, checking the spelling.

Words Ending in er

Add **er** to these words to find out what people do. If the word ends in **e**, e.g., dance, then just add **r**.

read _ _ teach _ _ dance _

climb _ _ play _ _ paint _ _

write _ bake _ sing _ _

Note for parent: There are many more — together you could make a list of further examples.

More Words with er

If a word has a vowel before the final consonant, we double the consonant before adding **er**.

For example:

swim → swimm**er**

run _ _ _

jog _ _ _

drum _ _ _

swim _ _ _

thin _ _ _

fat _ _ _

Note for parent: Words such as smaller and taller have a similar spelling pattern.

Adverbs: ly Endings

Draw lines to join **what** was said to **how** it was said.

"I have lost,"

"They stole it!"

"We want more!"

"I want to go to bed,"

"Woof! Woof!"

the toddler said sleepily.

the dog barked playfully.

we said angrily.

she said sadly.

they said hungrily.

Note for parent: This activity introduces adverbs – which tell us more about the verb in the sentence.

Suffix: ness

Add the suffix **ness** to the following words.

loud _ _ _ _ playful _ _ _ _
cheap _ _ _ _ late _ _ _ _
sick _ _ _ _ sad _ _ _ _
great _ _ _ _ smooth _ _ _ _

If a word ends in **y**, you need to change the **y** to **i** before adding **ness**.

For example: happy → happi**ness**

clumsy → clums _ _ _ _ _

Choose from the words above to complete each sentence.

The ______________ of the thunder scared us all.

Kittens are known for their ______________.

Some people get travel ______________.

She cried with ______________ when she won.

Note for parent: Refer to the last sentence and discuss why people may sometimes "cry with happiness."

Introducing Syllables

Count the syllables (or beats) in these words as you sound them out.

For example: **dog** has one syllable.
el/e/phant has three.

Draw lines in the words to separate the syllables.

umbrella

snowman

spider

mug

jellyfish

wardrobe

holiday

octopus

Note for parent: Use the word "beat" instead of syllable, if you prefer, and count the beats in each word as you sound it out.

Clap Our Names

Read the names on the class list.
Clap the syllables in each name.

For example: **Cin/de/rell/a**
has four beats!

Ava	Mohammad
Emma	Nazeem
Isabella	Olivia
Jim	Alexander
Sofia	Liam

Note for parent: Try your child's name first. Do you know any longer names? Rumpelstiltskin has four syllables!

Tricky Words

Read and try to remember what these tricky words look like.

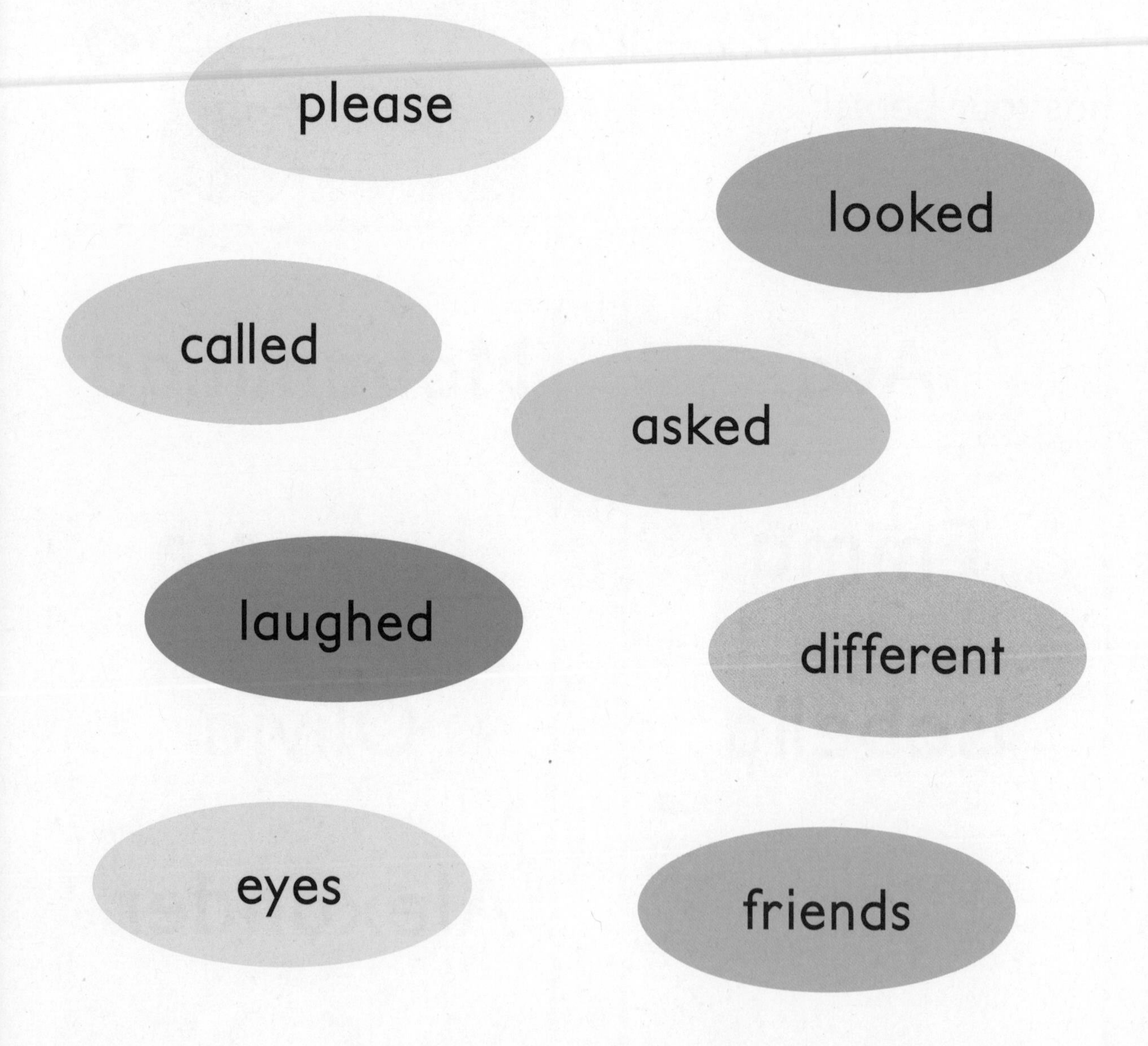

You can test how well you have remembered them on the opposite page. First, you must cover this page.

Note for parent: There is no easy way of learning these words. But with practice and familiarity your child will begin to recognize them on sight.

Tricky Test

Which is correct? Circle the correct word.

pleese or please

lucked or looked

called or cawled

asked or askt

laught or laughed

different or differant

eyes or eiys

friends or frends

Note for parent: This activity will help your child revise some tricky words that are commonly misspelled.

Prefix: un

The prefix un changes the root word to its opposite.

lucky → **un**lucky

Write **un** before the start of these words.

_ _ well	_ _ tidy
_ _ even	_ _ fair
_ _ happy	_ _ kind

Choose words from the list above to complete these sentences.

Cinderella was ____________ because the stepsisters were ____________ to her.
She had to do all the housework.
It was ____________.
The stepsisters were very ____________.
They left all their clothes for Cinderella to pick up!

Note for parent: Discuss which words will best fit in the spaces.

Prefix: re

If we put **re** before a verb it means the action will happen again.

For example: **re**do – to do again

Write **re** before these verbs.

_ _ pay	_ _ mix
_ _ fill	_ _ fuel
_ _ think	_ _ wind
_ _ name	_ _ call

Note for parent: Discuss the meanings of these words and try to think of examples from your child's own experiences.

Sounds the Same

Some words sound the same but are spelled differently and mean different things.

Read these words:

mail – male

plaice – place

new – knew

sow – sew

witch – which

threw – through

Choose a word from the list above to complete each sentence. Write the word in the space.

I have __________ school shoes.

A boy is a __________ child.

The __________ flew on a broomstick.

It was a fun __________ to visit.

She __________ the ball.

Note for parent: These words are more examples of homophones – words that sound the same but are spelled differently and have different meanings.

Sounds the Same: Word Search

Find 21 homophones in the word search. Look across and down. Draw a circle around each word you find.

b	p	l	a	c	e	s	s	v	s
n	l	d	d	w	h	e	r	e	o
m	a	i	l	m	a	l	e	e	w
a	i	d	r	w	e	r	e	r	w
i	c	t	h	r	o	u	g	h	r
n	e	h	e	t	a	i	l	r	w
m	t	e	i	c	z	z	n	e	i
a	d	r	r	d	k	n	e	w	t
n	w	e	a	r	s	e	w	b	c
e	t	a	l	e	w	h	i	c	h

tail tale mail male main mane
sow sew witch which their there
threw through place plaice new
knew where were wear

Note for parent: Here are some more homophones. Discuss the different spellings and meanings.

Answers

Page 10
s for sun and snail, a for airplane/ant, t for tree, p for parrot, i for insect/ice cream

Page 12
n for net,
m for motorbike,
d for duck,
n – nest, nuts, nail;
m – map, monkey, mouse;
d – dolphin, dog, drum

Page 13
pan and pan are exactly the same.
mat – at,
pin – tin – din – in,
pan – man,
dad – sad – pad

Page 15

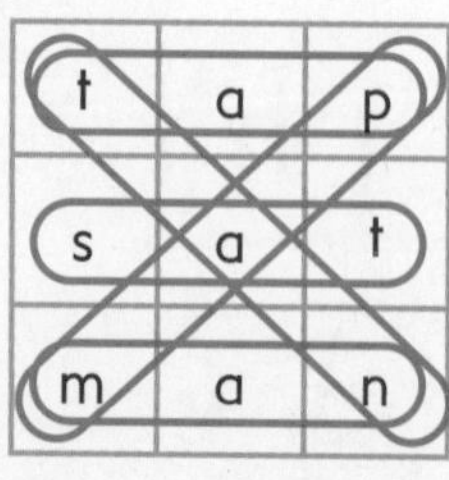

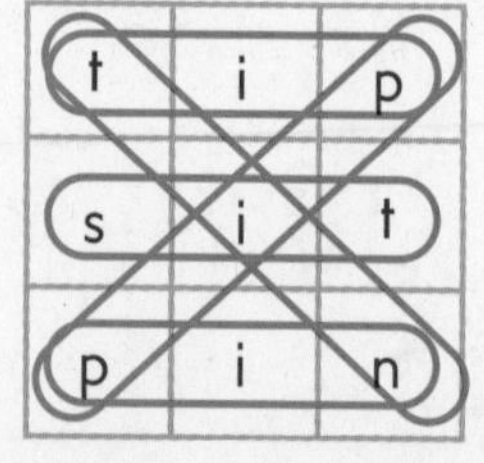

Page 16
g – goat, gate;
o – orange, owl;
c – car, cup;
k – kite, key

Page 18
e for egg,
u for umbrella,
r for robot
pen, red, sun, rug, ten, cup, net, nut

Page 19
tick – pick,
tack – rack,
tuck – duck,
rock – tock,
peck – deck

Page 20
l for leaf, h for horse,
b for bag, f for fox

Page 21
l – ladder, leaf, lion,
h – hat, hen, house,
b – bat, bed, bus,
f – feather, fish, fly

Page 22
h-op – hop, f-ig – fig,
b-it – bit, t-en – ten,
l-ap – lap, m-um – mum

Page 27
Hickory, dickory, dock,
The mouse ran up the clock,
The clock struck one,
The mouse was gone,
Hickory, dickory, dock!

Page 29
cats and dogs,
bats and balls,
pots and pans,
cups and mugs,
hens and eggs

Page 30
The doll is not in his suitcase!

Page 31
ten, dog, pip, fan, mop, lock

Page 32
Real words – at, on, am, in, up, if

Page 33
Ip is from Inland,
Og is from Onland

Page 34
j for jelly, v for vase,
w for watch,
x for x-ray

Page 35
Jack and Jaws,
Raj and Rav,
Tim and Tom,
Pip and Pop,
Vin and Van,
Bex and Bix,
Meg and Mug

Page 36
y for yo-yo,
z for zebra

Page 37
quiver, quake,
quarrel, quibble,
quick, quack, quiet,
quite, quest, queue

Page 38
a, b, c, d, e, f, g, h,
i, j, k, l, m, n, o, p, q,
r, s, t, u, v, w, x, y, z

Page 40
shell, chin, fish,
chimp, teeth, church

Page 46
three, goats, bridge

Page 50
ng – king, ring,
nd – hand, sand,
st – step, star

Page 52
wh for whale,
ph for phone

Page 54

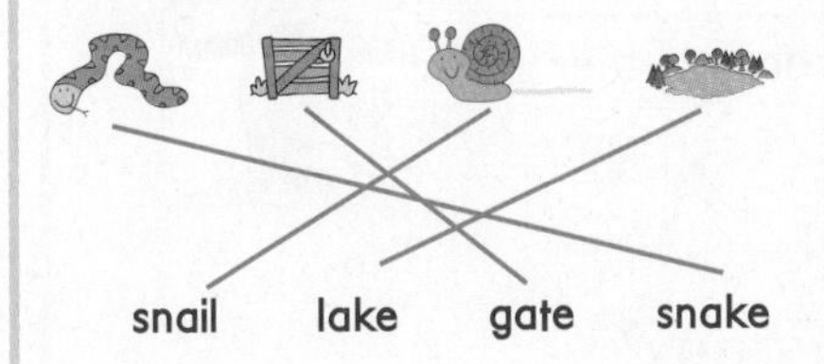

Page 55
pain and pane,
main and mane

Page 59
Jean, bean, beans, be,
green
(ea in meant is a
different sound)

Page 60
head, bread,
feather, thread,
weather, meadow

Page 61
spike, rice, slice, mike,
ice, bike, like, hike,
nice, trike

Page 62
plume, spine, tone, robe,
cane, cape, cute, huge,
plane, tape, cube, tube

Page 64
night, fright, light, bright,
tight, sight, lightning,
frightening, fight, all right

Page 67
stone, bone, cone, moan,
phone, groan, throne,
zone, tone, ozone

Answers

Page 71
front door, apple core,
clean floor, food store,
sea shore, big score
wild boar, lion's roar,
dog's paw, shark's jaw

Page 72
said, so, some,
come, have, like,
little, there

Page 74
hare – hair,
stair – stare,
fair – fare,
pear – pair,
bear – bare
long hair,
fluffy hare,
a pair of shoes,
a pear tree

Page 75
square, high chair,
mare, nightmare,
swimwear, footwear

Page 76

Page 77
desktop, ladybug,
airplane, football,
bathroom, rainbow,
raincoat, teacup

Page 78
loud, cloud, found,
sound, round,
ground, scout, sprout,
mountain, fountain

Page 79
sprout, cloud,
found, fountain,
ground, round

Page 81
oil, boil, soil, coin,
spoil, join, voice

Page 83
were, do, out,
one, when, what,
water, work, once

Page 85
crew – stew – new – few,
blue – glue, boot – root,
noon – soon – tune –
dune, tube – cube

Page 86
fudge, hedge, bridge,
badge

Page 88
kettle, nettle, cattle, little,
bottle, rattle

Page 91
gobble – wobble,
cobble, nobble,
hobble, bobble,
bumble – humble
rumble, mumble, jumble,
tumble
gaggle and goggle do
not rhyme

Page 92
knife, comb, knot, knit, know, kneel, knock

Page 93
A garden ornament: gnome
A small biting insect: gnat
A joint in the arm: wrist
Not right: wrong
To make words: write
To bite and chew: gnaw

Page 94
A sunny day
A happy birthday
A funny clown
A hairy goat
A bony skeleton
A scary monster

Page 95
A happy baby
A messy puppy
A silly daddy
A busy mommy
A pretty fairy
A fluffy bunny

Page 99
people, their, where, who, again, though, through, many, because, any

Page 101
string, strong, stream, street, screw, scrape, scream, shrimp, stitch

Page 102
KEEP OFF THE GRASS, EXIT, DANGER KEEP OUT!, WET PAINT, TOILETS, TOWN CENTER

Page 103
WELCOME, HOUSE, RIVER, TEA, CAR, AIRPORT

Page 104
station, education, imagination, relations

Page 106
dogs, hats, flowers, stars, trees,
chairs, books, umbrellas
watches, boxes, dishes, glasses, patches, splashes,
foxes, kisses

Page 107
fairies, ponies, bunnies, knives, wives, lives

Page 108
eating, jumping, crawling
dancing, baking, racing, riding, skating, waving, writing

Page 109
skipping, hopping, swimming, digging, cutting, clapping, dripping, drumming

Page 110
walked, looked, cooked, pushed, pulled, helped, skipped, shopped

Page 112
reader, teacher, dancer, climber, player, painter, writer, baker, singer

Answers

Page 113
runner, jogger, drummer, swimmer, thinner, fatter

Page 114
"I have lost," she said sadly.
"They stole it!" we said angrily.
"We want more!" they said hungrily.
"I want to go to bed," the toddler said sleepily.
"Woof! Woof!" the dog barked playfully.

Page 115
loudness, playfulness, cheapness, lateness, sickness, sadness, greatness, smoothness, clumsiness
The loudness of the thunder scared us all.
Kittens are known for their playfulness.
Some people get travel sickness.
She cried with happiness when she won.

Page 116
um/brell/a, snow/man, spi/der, mug, jell/y/fish, ward/robe, hol/i/day, oct/o/pus

Page 117
A/va, Emm/a, Is/a/bell/a, Jim, So/fi/a, Mo/hamm/ad, Na/zeem, O/liv/i/a, Al/ex/an/der, Li/am

Page 119
please, looked, called, asked, laughed, different, eyes, friends

Page 120
unwell, untidy, uneven, unfair, unhappy, unkind
Cinderella was unhappy because the stepsisters were unkind to her. She had to do all the housework.
It was unfair. The stepsisters were very untidy.

Page 121
repay, remix, refill, refuel, rethink, rewind, rename, recall

Page 122
new, male, witch, place, threw

Page 123

b	p	l	a	c	e	s	s	v	s
n	l	d	d	w	h	e	r	e	o
m	a	i	l	m	a	l	e	e	w
a	i	d	r	w	e	r	e	r	w
i	c	t	h	r	o	u	g	h	r
n	e	h	e	t	a	i	l	r	w
m	t	e	i	c	z	z	n	e	i
a	d	r	r	d	k	n	e	w	t
n	w	e	a	r	s	e	w	b	c
e	t	a	l	e	w	h	i	c	h